How to Pass

HIGHER
Chemistry

John Anderson

HODDER
GIBSON
AN HACHETTE UK COMPANY

The Publishers would like to thank the following for permission to reproduce copyright material:

Photo credits

p. 37 © Africa Studio - Fotolia.com; p. 60 (top) © Marius Graf - Fotolia.com, (bottom) © baibaz – Fotolia.com; p. 63 © Sheila Terry/Science Photo Library

Acknowledgements

Extracts from past exam papers are reproduced with the permission of the Scottish Qualifications Authority (© Scottish Qualifications Authority).

Every effort has been made to trace all copyright holders, but if any have been inadvertently overlooked the Publishers will be pleased to make the necessary arrangements at the first opportunity.

Although every effort has been made to ensure that website addresses are correct at time of going to press, Hodder Gibson cannot be held responsible for the content of any website mentioned in this book. It is sometimes possible to find a relocated web page by typing in the address of the home page for a website in the URL window of your browser.

Hachette UK's policy is to use papers that are natural, renewable and recyclable products and made from wood grown in sustainable forests. The logging and manufacturing processes are expected to conform to the environmental regulations of the country of origin.

Orders: please contact Bookpoint Ltd, 130 Park Drive, Milton Park, Abingdon, Oxon OX14 4SE. Telephone: (44) 01235 827720. Fax: (44) 01235 400454. Lines are open 9.00–5.00, Monday to Saturday, with a 24-hour message answering service. Visit our website at www.hoddereducation.co.uk. Hodder Gibson can be contacted direct on: Tel: 0141 333 4650; Fax: 0141 404 8188; email: hoddergibson@hodder.co.uk.

© John Anderson 2014

First published in 2014 by
Hodder Gibson, an imprint of Hodder Education,
An Hachette UK Company
211 St Vincent Street
Glasgow G2 5QY

Impression number 4

Year   2018 2017

Cover photo © auris - Fotolia
Illustrations by Aptara, Inc.
Typeset in 13/15 Cronos Pro (Light) by Aptara, Inc.
Printed in India
A catalogue record for this title is available from the British Library
ISBN: 978 1471 80828 9

Contents

Introduction

This book is designed to help students prepare for the CfE Higher Chemistry exam. It can be used as a complete summary of the course as it follows the 2014 SQA arrangements document.

The key to success in Higher Chemistry is to learn, understand and then practise. To help with this, each chapter contains worked examples which guide the student through chemical concepts. Hints and tips in each chapter offer sound advice on what should be learned, how to learn and how to apply chemical knowledge. In addition, each chapter concludes with a summary of the key points and a series of questions to enable students to test their understanding of the concepts covered. To help the student prepare for the exam, the end of chapter questions contain past SQA Higher exam questions which have been selected to test knowledge and understanding of the chemistry presented in the chapter.

Exam details

The Higher exam lasts 2½ hours and has two sections:
- Section A contains 20 multiple choice questions and is worth 20 marks.
- Section B contains restricted and extended response questions and is worth 80 marks.

Students should be able to demonstrate confidence with numeracy and analysis of data. In addition, the Higher exam contains two open-ended questions. Further advice and examples of the application of numeracy, and hints and tips on handling open-ended questions, are given in Appendix 1 at the end of this book.

Unit 1 Chemical Changes and Structure

Chapter 1
Controlling the rate

Measuring the rate of reaction

You will be well aware from carrying out experiments in the laboratory that chemical reactions occur at different rates. Measuring the **rate of reaction** allows chemists to compare reactions. For example, when marble chips (calcium carbonate, $CaCO_3$) are added to dilute hydrochloric acid (HCl), carbon dioxide gas (CO_2) is produced as shown in Figure 1.1.

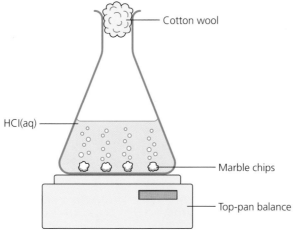

Figure 1.1 CO_2 is produced when marble chips react with HCl(aq).

The graph shown in Figure 1.2 shows how the **concentration** of acid changes as this reaction progresses.

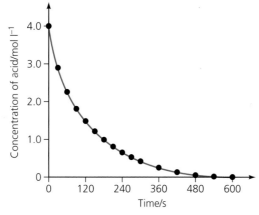

Figure 1.2 The concentration of acid decreases as the reaction progresses.

The rate of reaction can be calculated using the equation:

Remember

$$\text{rate of reaction} = \frac{\text{change in concentration}}{\text{time}}$$

Example

Using the graph in Figure 1.2, calculate the rate of reaction between
a) 0 and 120 s
b) 120 and 180 s.

Solution

a) Rate $= \dfrac{4 - 1.5}{120} = 0.02$ mol l^{-1} s^{-1}

b) Rate $= \dfrac{1.5 - 1.0}{60} = 0.08$ mol l^{-1} s^{-1}

When calculating rate of reaction, it is common to measure something that is related to the change in concentration. In the case of the experiment shown in Figure 1.1, CO_2 escapes from the flask. The reaction rate could be measured in terms of change in mass of the experimental apparatus or, if a gas syringe was connected to the flask as shown in Figure 1.3, the change in volume of gas released.

Remember

$$\text{rate of reaction} = \frac{\text{change in mass}}{\text{time}} \quad or \quad \frac{\text{change in volume}}{\text{time}}$$

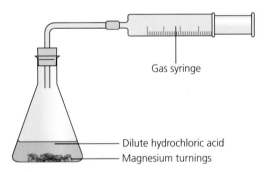

Gas syringe

Dilute hydrochloric acid
Magnesium turnings

Figure 1.3 A gas syringe can be used to measure the volume of gas released in a chemical reaction; in this case, the reaction is between hydrochloric acid and magnesium.

Example

The graph in Figure 1.4 shows how the mass of CO_2 released from the experiment changes as the reaction progresses. Calculate the rate of reaction between 0 and 360 s.

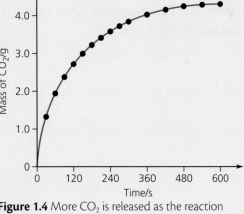

Figure 1.4 More CO_2 is released as the reaction progresses.

Solution

$$\text{Rate} = \frac{4.0 - 0.0}{360} = 0.011 \text{ g s}^{-1}$$

Where it is difficult to measure a change in the chemical reaction, the time for the reaction is used to calculate the **relative rate** of reaction, using the equation:

Remember

$$rate = \frac{1}{time}$$

For example, a reaction that took 20 s to reach completion would have a relative rate of

$$\frac{1}{20} = 0.05 \text{ s}^{-1}$$

If you know the relative rate of a reaction, you can calculate the time taken for the reaction using the equation:

Remember

$$time = \frac{1}{rate}$$

Example

Using the graph shown in Figure 1.5, calculate the time taken for the reaction when the temperature was 45 °C.

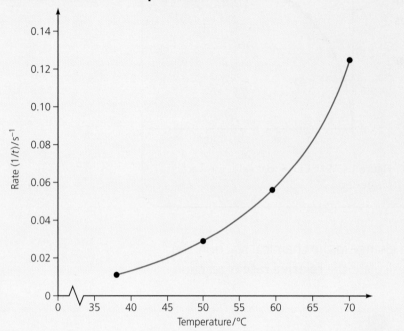

Figure 1.5 A graph of relative rate versus temperature

Solution

At 45 °C, the relative rate is $0.02\,s^{-1}$.

$$time = \frac{1}{rate} = \frac{1}{0.02} = 50\ s$$

Hints & tips

Calculating the rate of reaction is like calculating the speed in a race where you would use the formula

$$speed = \frac{distance}{time}$$

For chemical reactions, you can use this equation too except the distance will be replaced by whatever is being measured: usually volume, mass or concentration.

The most common units for reaction rate are:
- Concentration, $mol\,l^{-1}\,s^{-1}$
- Volume, $cm^3\,s^{-1}$
- Mass, $g\,s^{-1}$
- Relative rate, s^{-1}.

Always be sure to check the units used. For example, if the mass was measured in kg you would express the rate as $kg\,s^{-1}$. If the time was measured in minutes, you might have $kg\,min^{-1}$.

Collision theory

For a successful chemical reaction to occur, reactant particles must collide. Some collisions result in a reaction, others do not. Successful collisions occur when:
- the **collision geometry** is correct and
- the particles have the right amount of energy.

Concentration and pressure

Increasing the concentration, or pressure, increases the rate of reaction because you have more particles in the same space. As more of these particles are moving about, you are more likely to have collisions. If the particles colliding have sufficient energy, a successful reaction will occur.

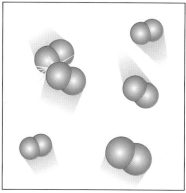
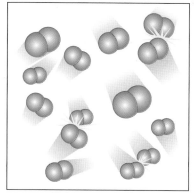

Lower concentration

Higher concentration

Figure 1.6 Particles are closer together if the concentration, or pressure, is increased. This leads to more collisions.

Particle size

Powdered solids react faster than lumps. Since it is only the particles on the surface of a solid that can react (since they are exposed), breaking up a solid into smaller pieces exposes more surfaces and hence more particles are available to react.

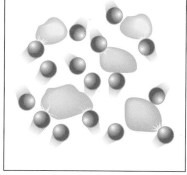

Smaller surface area

Larger surface area

Figure 1.7 Breaking up a solid into smaller particles increases the surface area leading to more collisions.

Temperature and activation energy

Raising the temperature of a reaction does more than simply increase the number of collisions between particles. Temperature is a measure of the average kinetic energy of the particles in a substance. If the temperature is increased, the particles have more kinetic energy. This means that they will collide with greater force.

It has been discovered that for a chemical reaction to occur, the colliding particles must have a minimum amount of kinetic energy. This minimum amount of energy is known as the **activation energy**. This concept helps to explain why some reactions do not occur at room temperature. For example, methane gas mixed with oxygen gas at room temperature does not react despite the particles colliding with each other. The particles do not have enough energy to react. To get the particles to react, some energy must be supplied (a spark or lit match will work).

a)   b)

Figure 1.8 a) Collision is not successful because the particles do not have enough energy.
b) Collision is successful as the particles do have enough energy.

In a gas, not all particles will have the same energy. *Energy distribution diagrams* can be used to show the energies of the particles. Figure 1.9 illustrates the distribution of kinetic energy and shows the minimum energy, activation energy, labelled E_A, required for a reaction to occur. The shaded area represents all of the **molecules** that have energy greater than the activation energy. In this example, very few particles have sufficient energy to react. This can be changed by giving the particles energy which can be done by increasing the temperature. Figure 1.10 shows that a small increase in temperature leads to a significant rise in the number of particles that have the minimum energy needed to react.

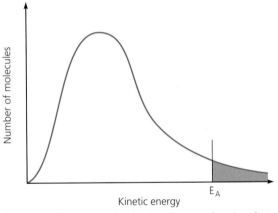

Figure 1.9 An energy distribution diagram showing that very few particles have enough energy to react.

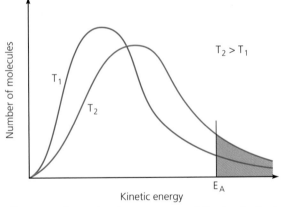

Figure 1.10 Increasing the temperature shifts the distribution curve to the right. Many more particles now have the minimum energy needed to react. The reaction rate increases.

Hints & tips ⭐

Know and understand the distribution curve shown in Figure 1.10 and remember that increasing the temperature leads to an increase in reaction rate because more particles now have energy greater than or equal to the activation energy.

Collision geometry

Collision geometry refers to the position of the reactants when they collide. Consider the reaction of propene with bromine as shown in Figure 1.11. Direct collision with the carbon to carbon double bond is more favourable and would be more likely to result in a reaction.

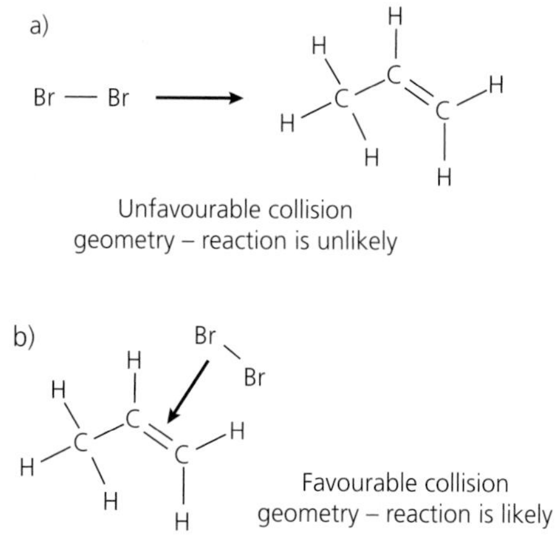

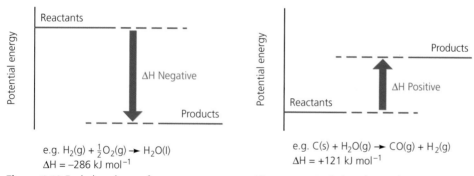

Figure 1.11 The collision geometry must be correct for a collision to be successful.

Reaction profiles

The energy change that occurs when reactants are converted into products is known as the **enthalpy change** (ΔH) and can be shown on potential energy diagrams as in Figures 1.12 and 1.13.

e.g. $H_2(g) + \frac{1}{2}O_2(g) \rightarrow H_2O(l)$
$\Delta H = -286$ kJ mol^{-1}

Figure 1.12 Enthalpy change for an exothermic reaction

e.g. $C(s) + H_2O(g) \rightarrow CO(g) + H_2(g)$
$\Delta H = +121$ kJ mol^{-1}

Figure 1.13 Enthalpy change for an endothermic reaction

In an **exothermic reaction** (Figure 1.12) the products have less energy than the reactants. Heat energy has been released to the surroundings. The ΔH for the reaction has a negative value to show that energy is 'lost' to the surroundings.

In an **endothermic reaction** (Figure 1.13) the products have more energy than the reactants as energy has been taken in from the surroundings. Removing heat energy from the surroundings causes the temperature of the surroundings to fall. Endothermic reactions have a positive ΔH to show that energy has been 'gained' from the surroundings.

Remember

$$\Delta H = Hproducts - Hreactants$$

Activation energy and the activated complex

Potential energy diagrams can be used to show the activation energy for a reaction, as shown in Figure 1.14.

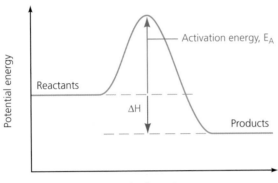

Figure 1.14 Potential energy diagram showing the activation energy and enthalpy change.

As a reaction proceeds from reactants to products, a very-high-energy species known as an **activated complex** is formed. This is an unstable arrangement of atoms which is very high in energy. In potential energy diagrams, the activated complex is shown at the very top of the activation energy barrier as illustrated in Figure 1.15.

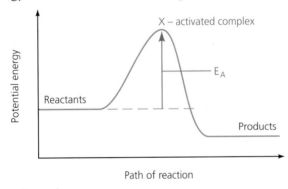

Figure 1.15 Activated complex

Catalysts

Catalysts speed up chemical reactions without being used up. Catalysts work by forming temporary bonds with reactants, causing the bonds within the reactants to weaken. This lowers the activation energy, allowing many more reactions to occur. The lowering of activation energy can be shown on a potential energy diagram as in Figure 1.16.

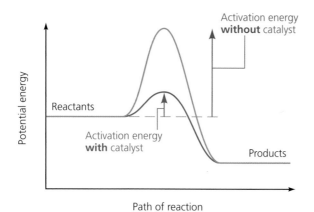

Figure 1.16 The lowering of the activation energy by a catalyst

Example

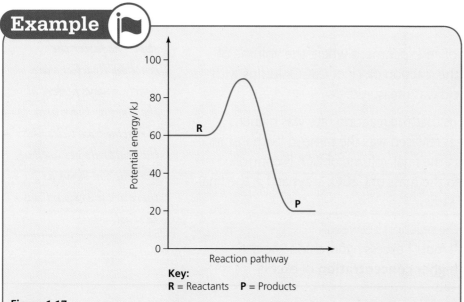

Figure 1.17

Key:
R = Reactants   **P** = Products

Using the potential energy diagram in Figure 1.17, calculate

a) ΔH for the forward reaction
b) ΔH for the reverse reaction
c) E_A for the forward reaction
d) E_A for the reverse reaction.
e) Suggest a value for the activation energy and enthalpy change for the forward reaction if a catalyst was used.
f) Suggest an energy value for the activated complex.

Solution

a) $\Delta H = H_{products} - H_{reactants} = 20 - 60 = -40\,kJ$
b) $\Delta H = H_{products} - H_{reactants} = 60 - 20 = 40\,kJ$
c) $E_A = 90 - 60 = 30\,kJ$
d) $E_A = 90 - 20 = 70\,kJ$
e) Any value lower than 30 kJ for E_A. The ΔH would still be 40 kJ as catalysts do not affect the enthalpy change.
f) 90 kJ

Reaction rate graphs

Look at the graph shown in Figure 1.18.

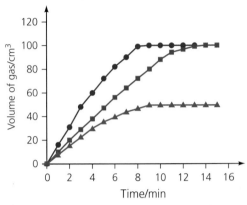

Figure 1.18 A graph showing rates of reaction for three versions of an experiment.

The red line shows the results of an experiment where the volume of carbon dioxide released from the reaction of 1g of $CaCO_3$ lumps with $1 \, mol \, l^{-1}$ excess hydrochloric acid was measured.

The blue line is steeper telling us that the reaction rate was higher; however, the final volume of gas released was the same in both instances: $100 \, cm^3$. As the acid is in excess, the final volume of CO_2 is controlled by the mass of $CaCO_3$. Provided the mass of $CaCO_3$ stays at 1g, the final volume of gas should stay the same.

The blue line could represent the reaction between:
- 1g of $CaCO_3$ **powder** with $1 \, mol \, l^{-1}$ excess hydrochloric acid
- 1g of $CaCO_3$ lumps with a **higher concentration** of excess hydrochloric acid
- 1g of $CaCO_3$ lumps with $1 \, mol \, l^{-1}$ excess hydrochloric acid at a **higher temperature**
- 1g of $CaCO_3$ lumps with $1 \, mol \, l^{-1}$ excess hydrochloric acid, using a **catalyst**.

The green line shows a final volume of gas which is half the original. We know that the volume of gas is controlled by the mass of $CaCO_3$, so the green line would be for the reaction of half the mass of $CaCO_3$ lumps with $1 \, mol \, l^{-1}$ excess hydrochloric acid, in other words, 0.5g.

Hints & tips

In Higher Chemistry, it can be useful to consider two things about rates of reaction graphs:

1 the gradient of the graph (the steepness)
2 where the graph ends.

The gradient tells you about the speed of the reaction: the steeper the slope, the faster the reaction. Reactions are nearly always fastest at the start as there are lots of reactant particles. As the reactants get used up, the reaction slows as there are fewer particles to react.

Key points

* The reaction rate can be calculated using the equations:

$$rate = \frac{change \ in \ concentration \ OR \ mass \ OR \ volume}{time}$$

or

$$rate = \frac{1}{time}$$

* Collision theory states that reactants must collide with the correct geometry and possess a minimum energy before a successful reaction occurs.
* Energy distribution diagrams help to explain why increasing the temperature significantly increases the reaction rate. ⇨

⇨
* Reaction profiles show the enthalpy change that occurs in a reaction and the activation energy.
* Exothermic reactions have a $-\Delta H$. Endothermic reactions have a $+\Delta H$.
* The activated complex is a high-energy, unstable arrangement of atoms. It is formed at the top of the activation energy barrier.
* Catalysts speed up a reaction by lowering the activation energy.

Study questions

1 Zinc was added to $25\,cm^3$ of hydrochloric acid, concentration $2\,mol\,l^{-1}$. Which of the following measurements, taken at regular intervals and plotted against time, would give the graph shown in Figure 1.19? The reaction is exothermic.
   A Temperature
   B Volume of gas produced
   C pH of solution
   D Mass of the beaker and contents

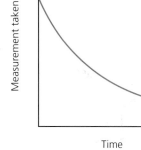

Figure 1.19

2 In which of the following will **both** changes result in an increase in the rate of a chemical reaction?
   A A decrease in activation energy and an increase in the frequency of collisions.
   B An increase in activation energy and a decrease in particle size.
   C An increase in temperature and an increase in the particle size.
   D An increase in concentration and a decrease in the surface area of the reactant particles.

3 Look at Figure 1.20.

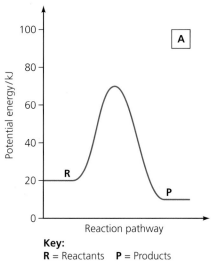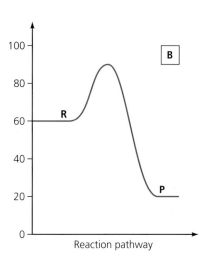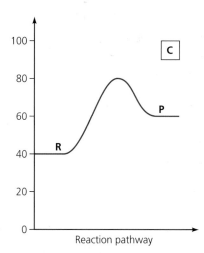

Key:
R = Reactants   P = Products

Figure 1.20

   a) Which reaction is likely to be the fastest?
   b) Which reaction is likely to have the most stable activated complex?
   c) Which reaction is endothermic?
   d) Which reaction has the greatest enthalpy change?
   e) Which reaction has an activation energy of 40 kJ?

⇨

4 The graph shows how the concentration of the hydrochloric acid changed over a period of time when the reaction was carried out at 20 °C. Calculate the average rate, in $mol\,l^{-1}$, in the first 400 minutes.

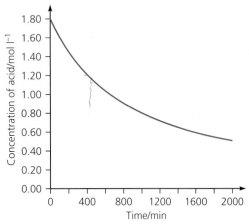

Figure 1.21

5 Which of the following descriptions describes how a catalyst works in a chemical reaction?
   A It supplies energy to the reactants.
   B It does not take part in the reaction.
   C It lowers the energy required to form an activated complex.
   D It lowers the enthalpy change for the reaction.

6 Figure 1.22 shows the results of several experiments in which excess zinc metal was reacted with sulfuric acid. The red line represents the reaction of lumps of zinc metal with $100\,cm^3$ of $1.0\,mol\,l^{-1}$ sulfuric acid at 23 °C.

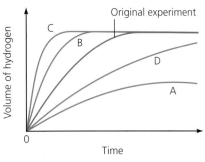

Figure 1.22

   a) Draw a diagram of the apparatus that could be used to measure the volume of gas produced in this experiment.
   b) Identify the line in the graph which shows the effect of
      i.   increasing the temperature
      ii. increasing the temperature and adding a catalyst
      iii. using $100\,cm^3$ of $0.5\,mol\,l^{-1}$ sulfuric acid at 23 °C
      iv. using $100\,cm^3$ of $1.0\,mol\,l^{-1}$ sulfuric acid at 13 °C.

Chapter 2
Structure and bonding in the first 20 elements

The structure and bonding in the first 20 elements of the **Periodic Table** is illustrated in Figure 2.1.

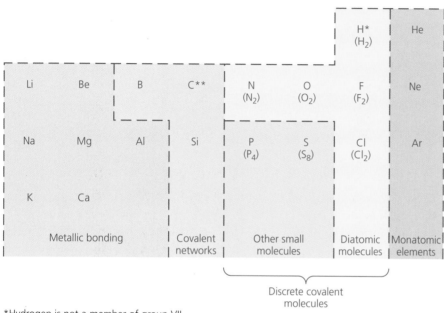

*Hydrogen is not a member of group VII
**Although unusually large, the fullerene forms of carbon are discrete covalent molecules

Figure 2.1 Summary of the structure and bonding in the first 20 elements of the Periodic Table

Metallic bonding

Metallic bonding consists of positive metal **ions** surrounded by a pool of **delocalised electrons**. The attraction between the charged metal ions and the **electrons** is known as metallic bonding. As this is a relatively strong attraction, metals typically have high melting points reflecting the energy required to overcome the strong metallic bonds. As the electrons are free to move, metals conduct electricity.

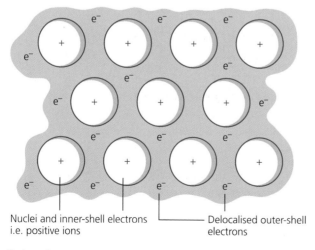

Nuclei and inner-shell electrons i.e. positive ions

Delocalised outer-shell electrons

Figure 2.2 Metallic bonding

Covalent molecular elements

Hydrogen, nitrogen, oxygen and the halogens are all examples of diatomic molecules consisting of two atoms joined by **covalent bonding**. Phosphorus, sulfur and the fullerenes are also **covalent molecular** in structure, but consist of much larger molecules.

- Phosphorus consists of four phosphorus atoms joined together by covalent bonds as shown in Figure 2.3.

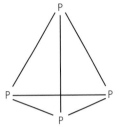

Figure 2.3 Phosphorus (P_4) molecule

- Sulfur can form molecules where eight sulfur atoms covalently bond to form 'puckered rings' as shown in Figure 2.4.

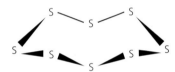

Figure 2.4 Bonding in sulfur (S_8)

- The fullerenes are a form of carbon consisting of five- and six-membered rings of carbon atoms covalently bonded together. One example of a fullerene consists of 60 carbon atoms, as shown in Figure 2.5.

For all of the covalent molecular elements, the *intra*molecular forces, the bonds within the molecule, are covalent. The *inter*molecular forces, those between the molecules, are the very weak **London dispersion forces**. (London dispersion forces are discussed in greater detail in Chapter 4.) Most of these elements have relatively low melting and boiling points since only the weak London dispersion forces have to be broken to melt and boil them. The heavier molecules, such as sulfur, phosphorus and the fullerenes, have many more electrons than the lighter molecules. Consequently, there are stronger London dispersion forces between the molecules, resulting in the higher melting points of these elements.

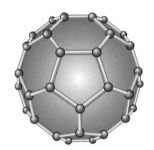

Figure 2.5 Fullerene structure (C_{60})

Covalent network elements

Unlike covalent molecular substances, which consist of only a few atoms bonded together, **covalent network** structures consist of many thousands of atoms joined together by covalent bonds. These structures have very high melting points as strong covalent bonds must be broken for the solid to melt.

Carbon diamond

Diamond is one form of carbon which is an example of a covalent network structure. Each carbon atom is covalently bonded to four other carbon atoms in a tetrahedral arrangement as shown in Figure 2.6. The resultant structure is exceptionally hard and strong. As all four outer electrons are used to form covalent bonds to other carbon atoms, carbon diamond does not conduct electricity.

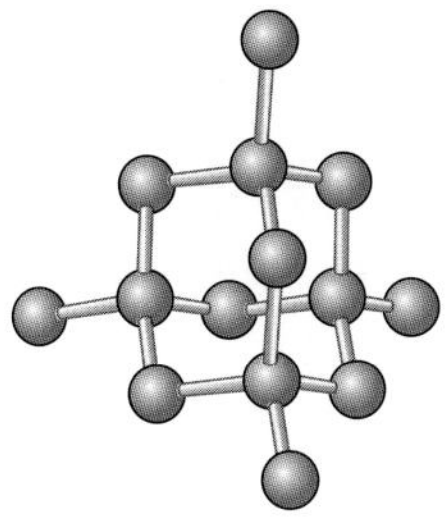

Figure 2.6 Diamond structure

Carbon graphite

In carbon graphite, each carbon atom forms three covalent bonds to neighbouring carbon atoms forming layers of hexagonal rings, as shown in Figure 2.7. The fourth outer electron becomes delocalised between the layers allowing carbon graphite to conduct electricity. The layers in graphite are held together by weak London dispersion forces. This allows the layers to move easily, making graphite an effective lubricant.

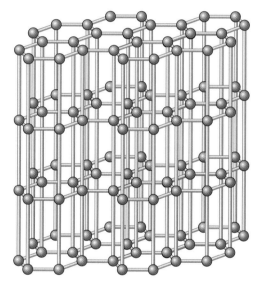

Figure 2.7 Graphite structure

Boron and silicon

Boron forms a covalent network structure based on B_{12} groups. Silicon forms a rigid covalent network with a similar tetrahedral structure to carbon diamond.

Monatomic elements

The noble gases are **monatomic** elements; they consist of single atoms which are not bonded to neighbouring atoms. When cooled, the atoms move closer together to form a liquid and then solid held together by weak London dispersion forces. As these forces are weak, the monatomic elements have very low melting points. As you descend the noble gases, the melting points increase as the London dispersion forces become stronger. This is due to the increased number of electrons.

Hints & tips ★

If you are asked to explain why one element has a higher or lower melting point compared to another element, always refer to the type of bonds or forces that must be overcome to melt the element. Relate this to the amount of energy that has to be supplied. This is illustrated in the worked example on page 16.

Example

Explain why sodium is a solid at room temperature whereas chlorine is a gas at room temperature.

Solution

This is the same question as: why does sodium have a higher melting point than chlorine?

To melt sodium, strong metallic bonds must be broken. Sodium is a solid at room temperature as there is not enough energy (at room temperature) to break the strong metallic bonds.

Chlorine molecules are held together by weak London dispersion forces. At room temperature, enough energy is supplied to overcome the London dispersion forces allowing the chlorine molecules to separate as a gas.

Key points

You should know how to describe the bonding and structures of the first 20 elements of the Periodic Table.

* Metallic: strong metallic bonds, high melting points, good conductors of electricity
* Covalent molecular: strong covalent bonds between atoms; weak London dispersion forces between molecules; sulfur, phosphorus and the fullerenes are solids as they are heavier molecules with more electrons, therefore they have stronger London dispersion forces between molecules
* Covalent network: strong covalent bonds between atoms; very high melting points as the strong covalent bonds must be broken; examples include carbon (diamond and graphite), silicon and boron.
* Monatomic: the noble gases are gaseous as they have weak London dispersion forces between atoms; melting points increase as you descend the group as the atoms have more electrons and therefore stronger London dispersion forces

Study questions

1 Figure 2.8 shows a representation of the first 20 elements.
   a) Which letter shows the monatomic elements?
   b) Which letter shows covalent network solids?
   c) Which letter shows diatomic covalent gases?
   d) Which letter represents elements which contain positive ions and delocalised electrons?

$\Rightarrow$

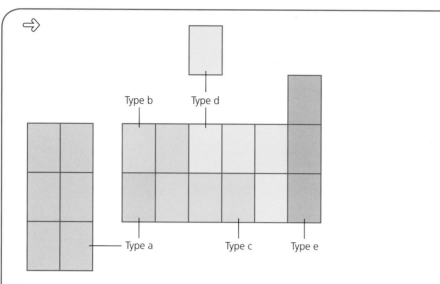

Figure 2.8

2 The melting and boiling points of the first 20 elements are shown in Figure 2.9.

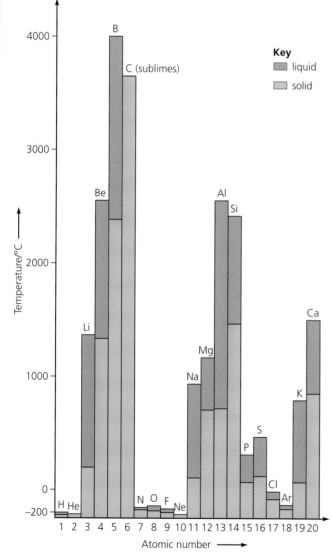

Figure 2.9

a) Why is there a significant difference between the melting points of Si and N?

b) Why does S have a higher melting point than Cl?

c) Why does K have a higher melting point than Ar?

3 When liquid oxygen evaporates
  A covalent bonds are formed
  B covalent bonds are broken
  C London dispersion forces are broken
  D London dispersion forces are formed.

4 Which element would require covalent bonds to be broken when it is melted?
  A Helium
  B Nitrogen
  C Boron
  D Sodium

5 Which of the following elements will not conduct electricity?
  A Potassium
  B Carbon graphite
  C Carbon diamond
  D Sodium

6 a) Copy and complete the table by adding the name of an element from elements 1 to 20 of the Periodic Table for each of the types of bonding and structure described.

Bonding and structure at room temperature and pressure	Name of element
Metallic solid	Sodium
Monatomic gas	
Covalent network solid	
Discrete covalent molecular gas	
Discrete covalent molecular solid	

  b) Why do metallic solids such as sodium conduct electricity?

Chapter 3
Trends in the Periodic Table

Covalent radius

The **covalent radius** is a measure of the size of an atom. It is half the distance between the nuclei of two covalently bonded atoms of an element, as shown in Figure 3.1.

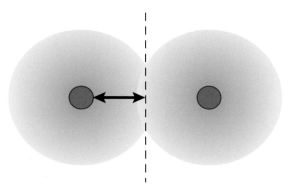

Figure 3.1 Half the distance between two nuclei is the covalent radius.

There are two general trends that are considered in Higher Chemistry:

Remember

1 *Going across a **period**, covalent radius decreases.*
2 *Going down a **group**, covalent radius increases.*

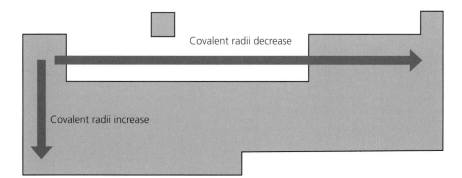

Covalent radii decrease

Covalent radii increase

Figure 3.2 Trends in covalent radius

The two factors that help explain these trends are the nuclear charge of the atom and the number of filled electron shells.

Going across a period: the effect of nuclear charge

Going across a period, the nuclear charge increases but the number of filled electron shells remains the same. This is shown in Table 3.1.

Table 3.1 The covalent radius decreases going across a period. Note that the unit of measurement here is picometres (pm), which is 1×10^{-12} m.

Element	Li	Be	B	C	N	O	F
Atomic number	3	4	5	6	7	8	9
Nuclear charge	3+	4+	5+	6+	7+	8+	9+
Electron arrangement	2,1	2,2	2,3	2,4	2,5	2,6	2,7
Covalent radius/pm	134	129	90	77	75	73	71

An increase in the nuclear charge results in electrons being more strongly attracted to the **nucleus** which means that the covalent radius decreases.

Going down a group: the shielding effect

Going down a group, the number of filled electron shells increases. This is shown in Table 3.2.

Table 3.2 The covalent radius increases going down a group.

Element	Li	Na	K	Rb	Cs
Atomic number	3	11	19	37	55
Nuclear charge	3+	11+	19+	37+	55+
Electron arrangement	2,1	2,8,1	2,8,8,1	2,8,18,8,1	2,8,18,18,8,1
Covalent radius/pm	134	154	196	216	235

Although the nuclear charge increases, its effect is outweighed by the much greater radius of adding electron layers. Each extra layer of electrons 'shields' the outer electrons from the positive nucleus so that the outer electrons are less strongly attracted to the nucleus. This results in an increase in covalent radius. This shielding effect is also known as **screening**.

Electronegativity

Electronegativity is a measure of attraction for electrons in a covalent bond. The higher the electronegativity value of an element, the stronger its attraction for electrons. For example, in a molecule of hydrogen chloride, the Cl attracts the shared electrons much more strongly than the H. Cl has an electronegativity value of 3.0 whereas H has a value of 2.2.

Figure 3.3 The Cl atom attracts the bonded electrons more strongly than the H atom in a molecule of hydrogen chloride.

The trends in electronegativity are:

Remember

1 Going down a group, electronegativity decreases.
2 Going across a period, electronegativity increases.

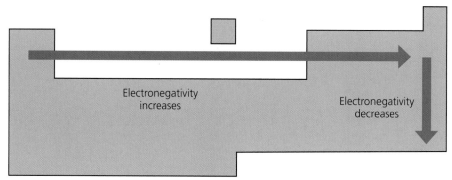

Figure 3.4 Trends in electronegativity

As with covalent radius, the two factors that influence electronegativity are the nuclear charge of an atom and the number of filled electron shells.

Table 3.3 Electronegativity increases across a period and decreases down a group.

H 2.2							
Li 1.0	Be 1.5	B 2.0	C 2.5	N 3.0	O 3.5	F 4.0	
Na 0.9	Mg 1.2	Al 1.5	Si 1.9	P 2.2	S 2.5	Cl 3.0	
K 0.8	Ca 1.0	Ga 1.6	Ge 1.8	As 2.2	Se 2.4	Br 2.8	
Rb 0.8	Sr 1.0	In 1.7	Sn 1.8	Sb 2.1	Te 2.1	I 2.6	
Cs 0.8	Ba 0.9						

decrease down group

increase across period

Going across a period, the nuclear charge increases. This increase in nuclear charge causes the atom to attract bonded electrons more strongly. Consequently, electronegativity increases across a period.

Going down a group, the number of filled electron shells increases. These extra electron shells screen the bonded electrons from the nuclear charge which means that electrons are less strongly attracted to the atom. Consequently, electronegativity decreases going down a group.

Ionisation energy

The **ionisation energy** is defined as 'the energy required to remove one **mole** of electrons from one mole of gaseous atoms'.

$$Na(g) \rightarrow Na^+(g) + e^- \qquad \Delta H = 502 \, kJ \, mol^{-1}$$

For sodium, 502 kJ of energy is required to remove the first electron from one mole of sodium atoms in the gaseous state. This is known as the first ionisation energy of sodium since it is a measure of the energy required to remove the first, or outermost, electron from sodium.

The second ionisation energy is the energy required to remove a second electron from sodium after the first electron has been removed.

$$Na^+(g) \rightarrow Na^{2+}(g) + e^- \qquad \Delta H = 4560 \, kJ \, mol^{-1}$$

The trends in first ionisation energy are:

Remember

1 Going down a group, the ionisation energy decreases.
2 Going across a period, the ionisation energy increases.

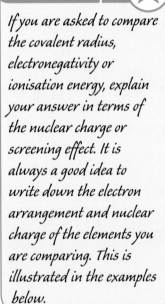

Hints & tips

If you are asked to compare the covalent radius, electronegativity or ionisation energy, explain your answer in terms of the nuclear charge or screening effect. It is always a good idea to write down the electron arrangement and nuclear charge of the elements you are comparing. This is illustrated in the examples below.

As with covalent radius and electronegativity, the factors that must be considered to help us explain the trends in ionisation energy are the nuclear charge of the atom and the number of filled electron shells.

Going across a period, the nuclear charge is increasing. The outermost electrons are therefore more strongly held and so the energy required to remove them, the ionisation energy, increases along each period.

Going down a group, an electron is being removed from the layer of electrons which is furthest from the nucleus. This layer is increasingly distant from the nuclear attraction and hence, although the nuclear charge is also increasing, less energy is required to remove an electron. An additional factor is the screening effect of electrons in inner shells. These inner electrons reduce the attraction of the nucleus for outermost electrons, hence reducing the ionisation energy.

Example

Explain why potassium has a lower first ionisation energy than lithium.

Solution

K: nuclear charge 19+; electron arrangement 2,8,8,1

Li: nuclear charge 3+; electron arrangement 2,1

Potassium has two extra filled layers of electrons compared with lithium. These extra layers screen the outer electron from the nucleus. Consequently, the outer electron in K is further from the nucleus and is not as strongly attracted (it is weakly held). It therefore takes less energy to remove the outer electron from K than it does to remove the outer electron from Li.

Example

Explain why the second ionisation energy of sodium is much higher than the first ionisation energy of sodium.

Solution

Na: electron arrangement 2,8,1

Removing the second electron from sodium involves breaking into the second shell of electrons which is much closer to the nucleus. Consequently, more energy is required as the electron in the second shell is more strongly attracted to the nucleus.

Key points

* Trends in the Periodic Table can be explained by comparing the nuclear charge or number of electron shells.
* An increase in nuclear charge causes the outer electrons to be more strongly attracted to the nucleus.
* An increase in the number of electron shells causes the outer electrons to be screened from the nucleus.

Study questions

1 Atoms of nitrogen and element X form a bond in which the electrons are shared equally. Element X could be
   A carbon
   B oxygen
   C chlorine
   D phosphorus.

2 A potassium atom is larger than a sodium atom because potassium has
   A a larger nuclear charge
   B a larger nucleus
   C more layers of electrons
   D a smaller ionisation energy.

3 Which of the following shows the correct equation for the second ionisation energy of potassium?

A $K(g) \rightarrow K^{2+}(g) + 2e^-$

B $K^+(g) \rightarrow K^{2+}(g) + 2e^-$

C $K^+(g) \rightarrow K^{2+}(g) + e^-$

D $K^{2+}(g) \rightarrow K^{3+}(g) + e^-$

4 Which statement correctly describes the reason for iodine having a larger covalent radius than fluorine?

A Iodine has a higher nuclear charge.

B Iodine has more layers of electrons.

C Iodine has a higher first ionisation energy.

D Iodine is more reactive than fluorine.

5 The elements from sodium to argon make up the third period of the Periodic Table.

a) On crossing the third period from left to right there is a general increase in the first ionisation energy of the elements.

i. Why does the first ionisation energy increase across the period?

ii. Write an equation corresponding to the first ionisation energy of chlorine.

b) The electronegativities of elements in the third period are listed in the databook. Why is no value provided for the noble gas argon?

6 a) Aluminium and phosphorus are close to one another in the Periodic Table but the P^{3-} ion is much larger than the Al^{3+} ion. Give the reason for this difference.

b) The P^{3-} ion and the Ca^{2+} ion have the same electron arrangement but the Ca^{2+} ion is smaller than the P^{3-} ion. Give the reason for this difference.

Structure and bonding

Pure covalent bonding

Diatomic elements such as hydrogen (H_2) exist as two atoms covalently bonded together. In other words, the two atoms *share* electrons. In the case of diatomic elements, both atoms have an equal 'pull' on the shared electrons (they have the same electronegativity) so we say that the bond is a *pure covalent bond* or a **non-polar covalent bond**.

Pure covalent bonding occurs in compounds where both atoms have the same electronegativity. For example in NCl_3, both N and Cl have an electronegativity value of 3.0 so the bond between the N and Cl is a non-polar covalent bond.

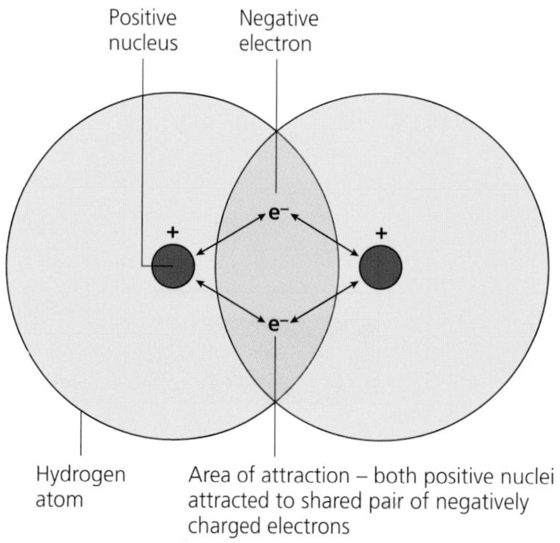

Figure 4.1 Two hydrogen atoms forming a covalent bond. This is a non-polar covalent bond since both H atoms have an equal attraction for the electrons in the bond.

Polar covalent bonding

In most compounds, the two atoms forming the covalent bond have different electronegativity values. In this case, the atom with the highest electronegativity attracts electrons more strongly than the other atom. This results in the atom with the higher electronegativity having a slight negative charge ($\delta-$) and the other atom having a slight positive charge ($\delta+$). This type of covalent bond is known as a **polar covalent bond**. In water, for example, the oxygen atom has a higher electronegativity than the hydrogen atom. In hydrogen chloride, the chlorine has a higher electronegativity than the hydrogen. This is illustrated in Figure 4.2.

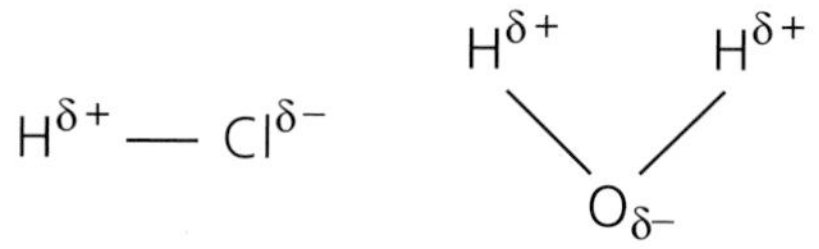

Figure 4.2 Hydrogen chloride and water have polar covalent bonds. This is caused by the atoms sharing the electrons having different electronegativity values.

Ionic bonding

Atoms with a large difference in electronegativity will sometimes form an **ionic bond**. An ionic bond does not involve sharing electrons; it occurs where electrons are transferred from one atom to another causing one atom to lose electrons (and become positively charged) and the other atom to gain electrons (and become negatively charged). The attraction between the positive ions of one element and the negative ions of the other element is known as an ionic bond. Typically, when a metal bonds with a non-metal, an ionic bond forms as the metal has a low electronegativity value and the non-metal has a much higher electronegativity value. This is a general rule and it should be remembered that some metal compounds will be covalent.

The bonding continuum

Some ionic compounds have stronger ionic properties than others and some covalent compounds have stronger covalent properties than others. When comparing compounds, the one with the greatest difference in electronegativity would usually be the 'most' ionic. The concept of a **bonding continuum** can be used to help us appreciate the differences in bonding, where pure ionic bonding and pure covalent bonding are at opposite ends and polar covalent bonding is in the middle. This idea is illustrated in Figure 4.3.

Compound	LiF	BeF_2	NF_3	OF_2	(F_2)
Difference in electronegativity	3.0	2.5	1.0	0.5	0.0

Ionic   Polar covalent   Covalent

Figure 4.3 The bonding continuum

Ionic or covalent bonding?

Electronegativity is one tool for deciding the type of bonding in a compound, but it is important to look also at the properties of the compound. There are three main characteristics of compounds that can be used to help decide whether the compound being studied is ionic or covalent:

1 Ionic compounds will conduct electricity when molten or when they are dissolved in water; covalent compounds will not conduct.
2 Ionic compounds tend to have high melting points as a lot of energy is required to break the strong ionic bonds that exist in the ionic **lattice** formed by such compounds in the solid state.
3 Ionic compounds are usually soluble in water.

The melting point of covalent compounds varies enormously as covalent compounds can exist in huge network structures with very high melting points (such as SiO_2, mp 1610 °C) or they can exist as small molecules with much lower melting points (such as CH_4, mp −182.5 °C).

Tin (IV) iodide is an example of a low melting point solid (144 °C) that does not conduct electricity when molten. Given this information we can conclude that tin (IV) iodide is a covalent compound. The fact that tin has an electronegativity value of 1.8 and iodine has an electronegativity value of 2.6 allows us to conclude that tin (IV) iodide contains polar covalent bonds.

Intermolecular forces and properties of compounds

Ionic compounds are held together in the solid state by ionic bonds. Covalent network compounds are held together in the solid state by covalent bonds. Covalent molecules, such as water or carbon dioxide, are held together in the solid state by forces of attraction known as **van der Waals' forces**. When we heat a solid compound such as water (ice), energy is required to break the van der Waals' forces which hold the molecules together.

There are three main types of van der Waals' force:
1 London dispersion forces
2 permanent dipole–permanent dipole interactions
3 hydrogen bonding.

Figure 4.4 summarises the properties of the three types of forces.

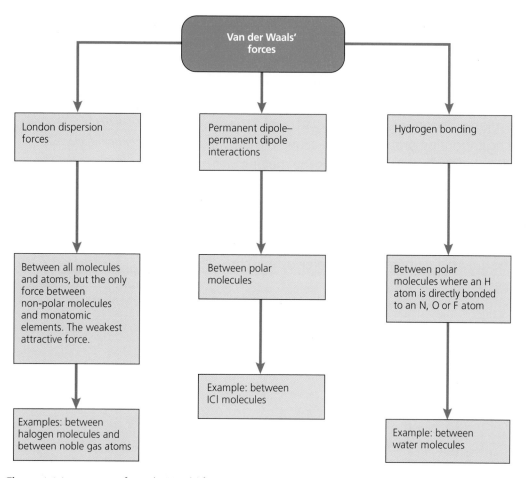

Figure 4.4 A summary of van der Waals' forces

London dispersion forces (LDF)

London dispersion forces are the weakest forces of attraction which can operate between atoms and molecules. They are caused by the uneven distribution of moving electrons. Figure 4.5 illustrates how this occurs in a monatomic element. The same principle can be applied to molecules.

Figure 4.5 shows the formation of **temporary dipoles** in which the side of the atom which has an excess of electrons becomes $\delta-$, causing the other side of the atom to become $\delta+$. The electrons in a neighbouring atom will shift away from an approaching $\delta-$ causing a $\delta+$ to appear. This is known as an *induced dipole* since one atom has caused this to happen to its neighbour. This sets up the attraction we call London dispersion forces.

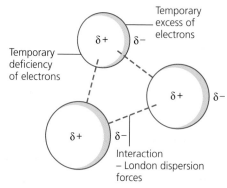

Figure 4.5 London dispersion forces

London dispersion forces are the main force between non-polar molecules.

Permanent dipole–permanent dipole interactions (pdp–pdp)

Permanent dipole–permanent dipole interactions occur between polar molecules and are much stronger than London dispersion forces. This can be illustrated by examining the polar molecule known as propanone, shown in Figure 4.6.

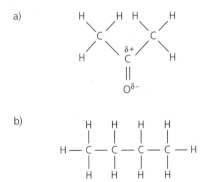

Figure 4.6 Propanone molecules bond to each other by pdp–pdp interactions.

The permanent dipole in one propanone molecule is attracted to the permanent dipole in a neighbouring propanone molecule. We know that this is stronger than London dispersion forces as the melting and boiling points of compounds that contain pdp–pdp interactions are much higher than those that contain London dispersion forces. For example, propanone can be compared to butane as both molecules have a similar number of electrons. Therefore, any difference in melting or boiling point must be due to an intermolecular force other than London dispersion forces.

a)

b)

Figure 4.7 a) Propanone: bp 56 °C, b) butane: bp 0 °C

Propanone has a much higher boiling point than butane. This tells us that it takes much more energy to break apart the attractions between propanone molecules than it does to break apart the attractions between butane molecules. Since propanone has pdp–pdp interactions and butane has LDF between molecules, the higher boiling point of propanone tells us that pdp–pdp interactions are much stronger than LDF.

Polar or non-polar molecules?

Most compounds that contain polar covalent bonds are, overall, polar molecules. In other words, the molecules that make up the compounds have a permanent dipole where one side of the molecule is $\delta+$ and the other side of the molecule is $\delta-$. Ammonia is a good example and is illustrated in Figure 4.8.

Figure 4.8 Ammonia is an example of a polar molecule.

Other molecules have a symmetrical arrangement of polar bonds causing the polarity to cancel. Carbon dioxide, **hydrocarbons** such as the **alkanes**, and tetrachloromethane are examples of non-polar molecules that have polar bonds which cancel.

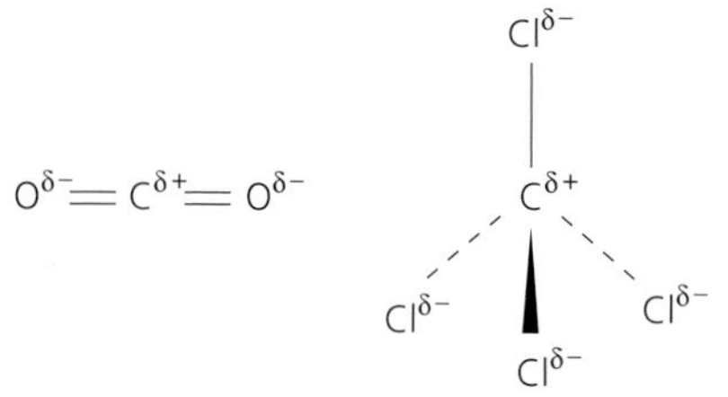

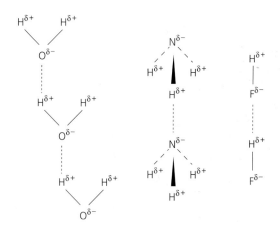

Figure 4.9 These molecules – carbon dioxide and tetrachloromethane – contain polar bonds but are, overall, non-polar molecules.

Hydrogen bonding

Hydrogen bonding is the strongest of the three intermolecular attractions. It occurs between molecules where there is an atom of H joined to an atom of N, O or F. The dashed lines in Figure 4.10 represent the hydrogen bonds between the molecules. Because these attractions are much stronger, hydrogen-bonded compounds have much higher melting and boiling points than would be expected.

> **Hints & tips** ⭐
>
> *Non-polar molecules will be held together by London dispersion forces whereas polar compounds will be held together by pdp–pdp interactions or hydrogen bonds.*

Figure 4.10 Hydrogen bonding in water, ammonia and hydrogen fluoride

Relating properties to intermolecular forces

Melting and boiling points

Differences in intermolecular forces of attraction give rise to compounds having different melting and boiling points. This is illustrated in the examples which follow.

Octane (C_8H_{18}) and methane (CH_4) are both non-polar covalent molecules. The main force of attraction between non-polar molecules is London dispersion forces. Octane has a much higher boiling point because it has more electrons and therefore the strength of LDF between octane molecules is greater than the strength of LDF between methane molecules. Consequently, more energy is required to break the LDF attraction between octane molecules and hence octane has a higher boiling point.

Hydrogen sulfide (H_2S) and water (H_2O) are both examples of polar molecules. The boiling point of water is much higher than the boiling point of hydrogen sulfide because water molecules are held together by hydrogen bonds whereas hydrogen sulfide molecules are held together by pdp–pdp interactions. Hydrogen bonding is stronger than pdp–pdp interactions, therefore it takes more energy to break apart the hydrogen bonds between water molecules than it does to break apart the pdp–pdp interactions between hydrogen sulfide molecules. Consequently, water has a higher boiling point.

Solubility

In general, polar solvents such as water can dissolve polar and ionic substances. (A polar solvent is one in which the ends of the molecules have slight positive ($\delta+$) and negative ($\delta-$) charges.) Polar and ionic substances will not dissolve in non-polar substances. For example, salt (NaCl) will dissolve easily in water but will not dissolve in the non-polar solvent heptane.

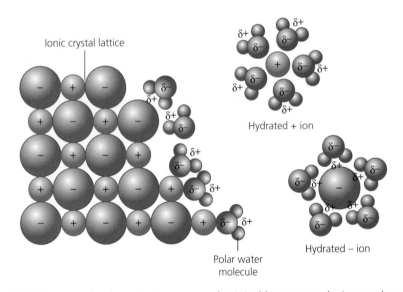

Figure 4.11 Water can dissolve an ionic compound as it is able to attract the ions as shown.

Non-polar compounds can dissolve in non-polar solvents but cannot dissolve in polar solvents. For example, wax (a non-polar hydrocarbon) can dissolve in hexane (a non-polar solvent) but will not dissolve in water (a polar solvent).

Example

Which two of the following compounds are likely to be soluble in water?

A ethanol

B hexane

C PH_3

D LiCl

Solution

Compound A is a polar molecule so is likely to dissolve in water.

Compound B is non-polar molecule so will not dissolve in water.

Compound C is a non-polar molecule so will not dissolve in water.

Compound D is an ionic compound so is likely to dissolve in water.

Viscosity

Viscous liquids have strong intermolecular forces between molecules. For example, when glycerol and ethanol are compared (Figures 4.12 and 4.13), glycerol is found to be a much more viscous liquid.

Ethanol has one hydroxyl (–OH) group whereas glycerol has three –OH groups. Consequently, hydrogen bonding between glycerol molecules is much stronger than the hydrogen bonding that can occur between ethanol molecules. Overall, increasing the number of **hydroxyl groups** in a molecule increases the **viscosity**.

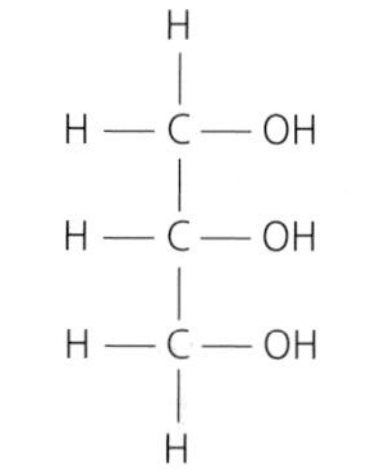

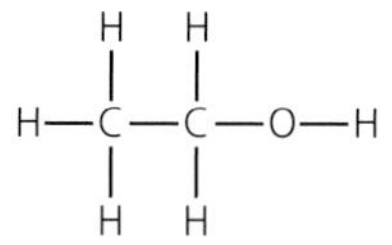

Propane-1,2,3-triol or glycerol

Figure 4.12 Glycerol

Figure 4.13 Ethanol

The density of ice

When most liquids become solids, the density of the solid is greater than that of the liquid since the particles in the solid state are packed much closer together compared to the particles in the liquid state. Water is unusual in that at its freezing point (the point at which it turns to ice), it is less dense than liquid water. This arises because the most efficient hydrogen bonding in ice comes from the water molecules adopting an arrangement known as an 'open-lattice' structure which results in lots of spaces between water molecules. The fact that ice is less dense than liquid water allows the solid ice to float on top of water.

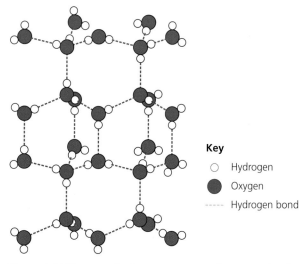

Key

○ Hydrogen

● Oxygen

----- Hydrogen bond

Figure 4.14 The open-lattice arrangement of water molecules in ice

Key points

* Polar covalent bonds are formed when two atoms with different electronegativity values form a covalent bond. The atom with the higher electronegativity value is assigned the symbol δ– and the atom with the lower value is assigned the symbol δ+.
* Non-polar covalent bonds are formed between two atoms with the same electronegativity value. The atoms have an equal attraction for electrons in the covalent bond.
* Compounds with polar bonds will form polar molecules provided the molecule is not symmetrical.
* Compounds with non-polar bonds will form non-polar molecules.
* Symmetrical compounds with polar bonds (such as CO_2) will form non-polar molecules.
* Non-polar molecules are attracted to other non-polar molecules by LDF.
* Polar molecules are attracted to other polar molecules by pdp–pdp interactions or hydrogen bonding.
* Permanent dipole–permanent dipole interactions occur between molecules where the molecule has a permanent dipole, for example between ICl molecules.
* Hydrogen bonding occurs between molecules that contain an atom of H bonded to an atom of N, O or F, for example between alcohol molecules.
* Molecules with stronger intermolecular forces will have higher melting and boiling points and a higher viscosity.
* Solubility can be predicted using the rule 'like dissolves like'. In other words, polar molecules and ionic substances will dissolve in polar solvents; non-polar compounds will dissolve in non-polar solvents.

Study questions

1 Which of the following compounds contain a polar covalent bond?
   A NaCl
   B CS_2
   C CO_2
   D NCl_3

2 Which of the following compounds is a non-polar covalent compound that contains a polar covalent bond?
   A $MgCl_2$
   B PH_3
   C HCl
   D CCl_4

3 Which of the following structures is *never* found in compounds?
   A Ionic
   B Monatomic
   C Covalent network
   D Covalent molecular

$\Rightarrow$

4 In which of the following solvents is lithium chloride most likely to dissolve?

   A Hexane

   B Benzene

   C Methanol

   D Tetrachloromethane

5 Hydrogen will form a non-polar covalent bond with an element which has an electronegativity value of

   A 0.9

   B 1.5

   C 2.2

   D 2.5.

6 Which property of a chloride would prove that it contained ionic bonding?

   A It conducts electricity when molten.

   B It is soluble in a polar solvent.

   C It is a solid at room temperature.

   D It has a high boiling point.

7 Figure 4.15 shows the trend in boiling points for four alkanes. Explain the trend.

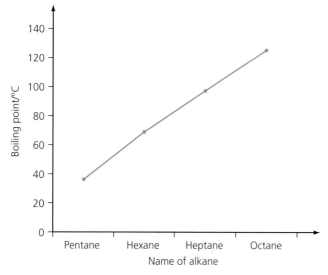

Figure 4.15

8 The melting points of the hydrogen compounds of groups 4, 5, 6 and 7 are shown in Figure 4.16.

  a Explain why H_2O, NH_3 and HF have much higher melting points than expected (when compared to other hydrogen compounds of similar mass).

  b Describe the **intermolecular bonding** in

    i. PH_3

    ii. H_2S.

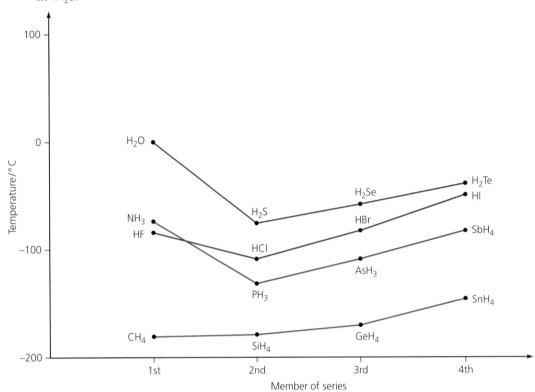

Figure 4.16

9 Liquid hydrogen sulfide has a boiling point of −60 °C. Explain clearly why hydrogen sulfide is a gas at room temperature. In your answer, you should name the intermolecular forces involved and indicate how they arise.

Figure 4.17

10 A student writes the following two statements. Both are *incorrect*. In each case explain the mistake in the student's reasoning.

  a) All ionic compounds are solids at room temperature. Many covalent compounds are gases at room temperature. This proves that ionic bonds are stronger than covalent bonds.

  b) The formula for magnesium chloride is $MgCl_2$ because, in solid magnesium chloride, each magnesium ion is bonded to two chloride ions.

Esters

Some of the most memorable smells come from compounds known as **esters**. Esters are formed by reacting an **alcohol** with a **carboxylic acid**. This reaction is known as a **condensation reaction** since the alcohol and carboxylic acid join together by eliminating water.

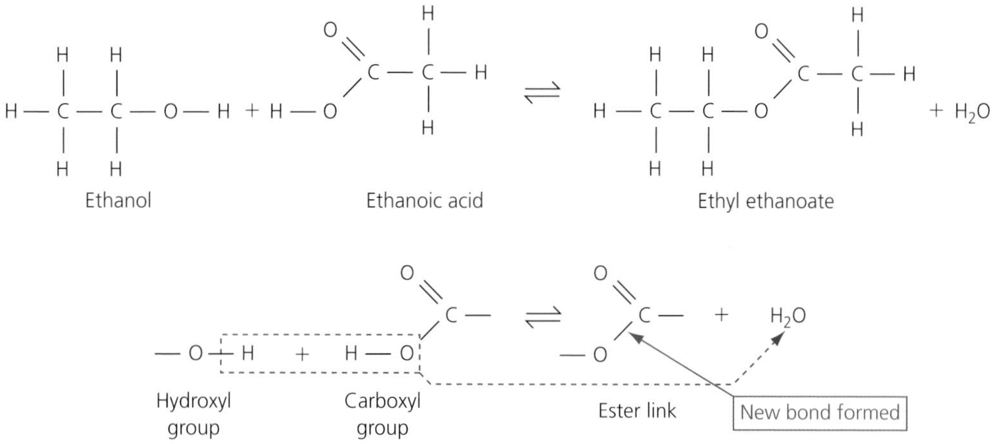

Figure 5.1 Forming an ester from ethanol and ethanoic acid

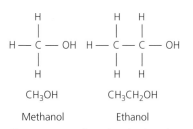

CH₃OH

Methanol

CH₃CH₂OH

Ethanol

CH_3OH CH_3CH_2OH

Figure 5.2 Methanol and ethanol are examples of alcohols. An H atom has been replaced by the –OH functional group.

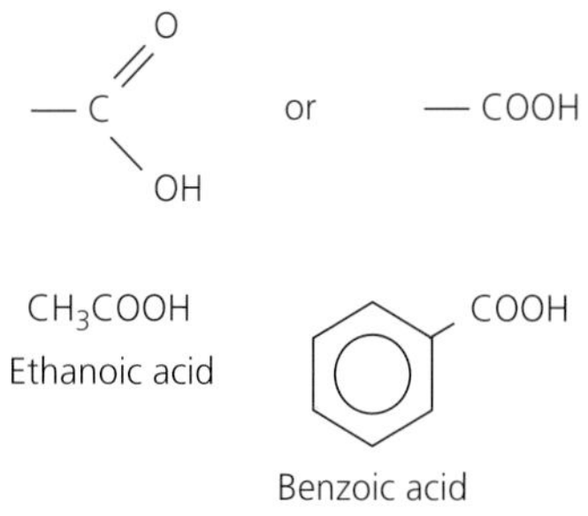

or   — COOH

CH_3COOH
Ethanoic acid

— COOH

Benzoic acid

Figure 5.3 The carboxyl functional group and some examples of carboxylic acids

Naming esters

Table 5.1 shows the names of some common esters, their structures and the alcohol and carboxylic acid from which they were made.

Table 5.1 Naming esters

Alcohol	Carboxylic acid	Ester formed
Methanol	Ethanoic acid	Methyl ethanoate
Ethanol	Propanoic acid	Ethyl propanoate
Ethanol	Butanoic acid	Ethyl butanoate

The first part of the ester name, which ends in '-yl', comes from the alcohol and the second part, which ends in '-oate', comes from the acid. Two examples are shown in Figures 5.4 and 5.5.

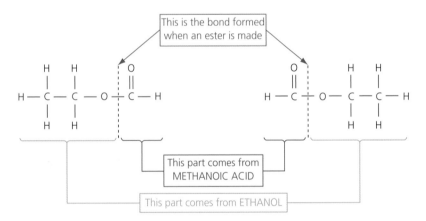

This is the bond formed when an ester is made

This part comes from METHANOIC ACID

This part comes from ETHANOL

Hence, this ester is called ETHYL METHANOATE

Figure 5.4 Naming an ester using full **structural formulae**

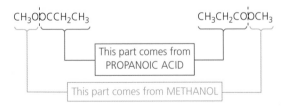

$CH_3OOCCH_2CH_3$ $CH_3CH_2COOCH_3$

This part comes from PROPANOIC ACID

This part comes from METHANOL

Hence, this ester is called METHYL PROPANOATE

Figure 5.5 Naming an ester using shortened structural formulae

Uses of esters

As many esters have a pleasant, fruity smell, they are often used in scented products such as deodorants and perfumes. Aside from this, esters are also used as solvents. They are able to dissolve a wide variety of compounds and they have relatively low boiling points allowing them to evaporate easily. They are found in everyday products such as nail varnish and spray paints.

Figure 5.6 Nail varnish contains the ester ethyl ethanoate as the solvent.

Example

1 Name the following esters:

a)   b)

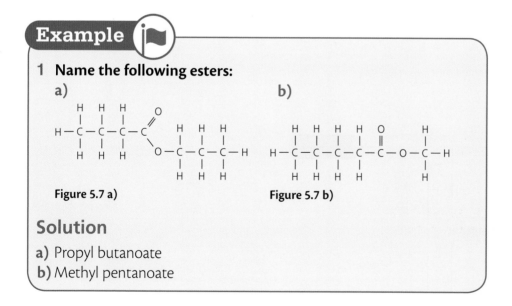

Figure 5.7 a)   **Figure 5.7 b)**

Solution

a) Propyl butanoate
b) Methyl pentanoate

Hydrolysis of esters

When an ester reacts with water, the ester breaks down to form an alcohol and carboxylic acid. This reaction is known as *ester hydrolysis*. For example, the ester methyl ethanoate will form methanol and ethanoic acid when it is hydrolysed. Table 5.2 shows the products formed when the ester is hydrolysed.

Table 5.2 Ester hydrolysis produces an alcohol and a carboxylic acid.

Ester	Alcohol formed	Carboxylic acid formed
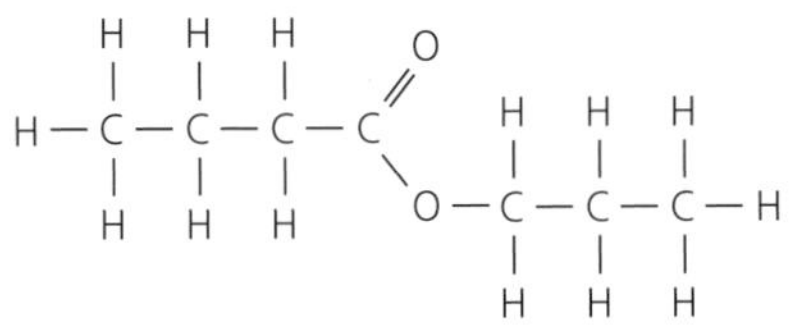	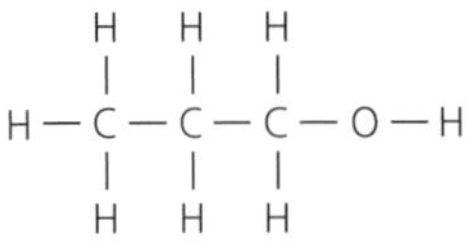	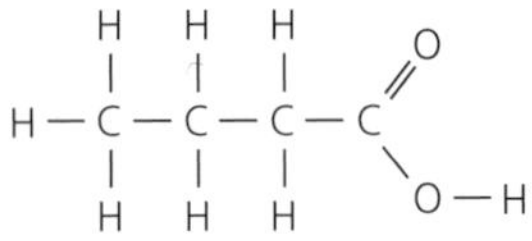
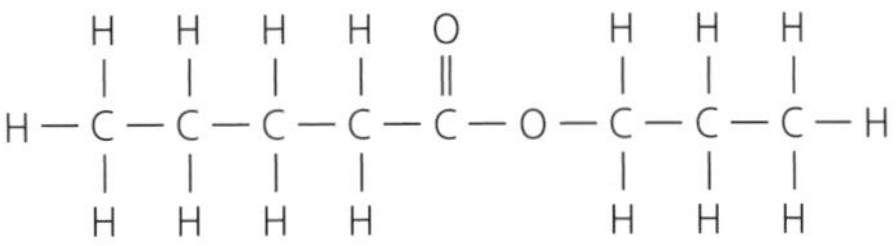	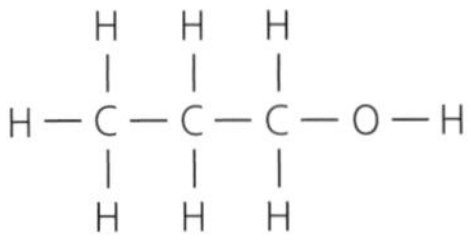	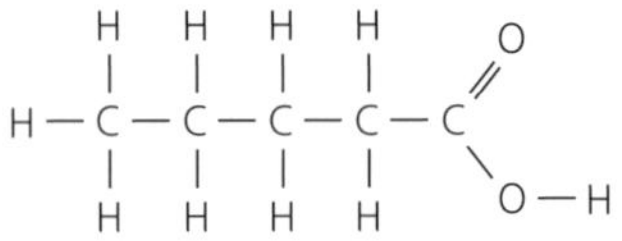

Fats and oils

Fats and **oils** are esters formed from the reaction of **glycerol** (an alcohol) and three **fatty acid** molecules. As glycerol has three –OH groups it can form three ester links with the fatty acid molecules. The product ester formed is a fat or oil and can be called a **triglyceride** because of the three ester links.

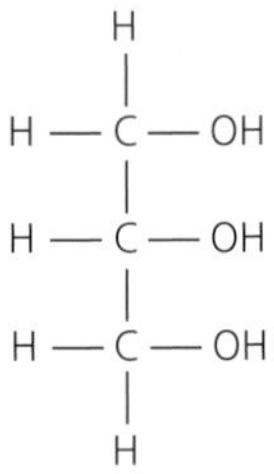

Propane-1,2,3-triol or glycerol
Figure 5.8 Glycerol is an alcohol with three –OH groups.

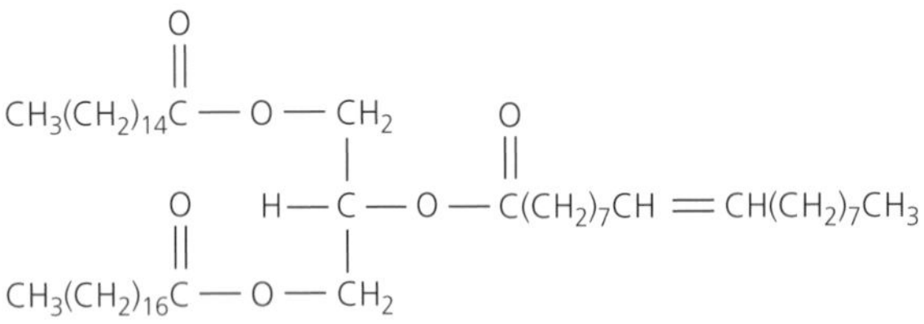

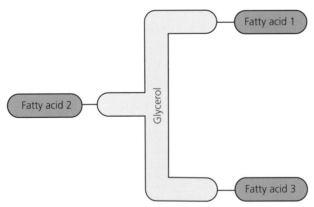

Figure 5.9 An example of a triglyceride; note the three ester links

Figure 5.10 The structure of a fat or oil

At room temperature fats are solid whereas oils are liquids. The structure of the fatty acids which join glycerol affects whether the triglyceride formed is a fat or an oil.

Remember

● Fats are formed from **saturated** fatty acids.
● Oils are formed from **unsaturated** fatty acids.

A high degree of saturation gives the fat molecules an even, regular structure which allows them to pack closely together, as shown in Figure 5.11. This efficient packing increases the number of van der Waals' attractions, making the attraction between fat molecules greater than the attraction between oil molecules. When the fat is heated, the van der Waals' attractions are broken and the fat melts.

Hints & tips

Saturated fats are Solid.

Figure 5.11 Fat molecules are able to pack closely together.

In oils, the double bonds cause the molecules to have an uneven, distorted structure, which makes it difficult for them to pack closely together, as shown in Figure 5.12. This results in fewer van der Waals' attractions between oil molecules. It therefore takes less energy to break apart the oil molecules which means that oils have a lower melting point than fats.

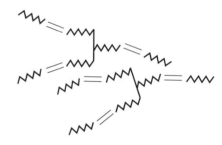

Figure 5.12 Oil molecules cannot pack closely together.

Hints & tips

Compared to other alcohols, glycerol is very viscous and has a high boiling point. Both properties are due to the fact that glycerol has three —OH groups. This allows glycerol molecules to form more hydrogen bonds between molecules than alcohols with only a single —OH group.

Fats and oils in the diet

As well as being a concentrated source of energy, fats and oils are an essential component of our diet as their non-polar structure allows them to dissolve a number of essential vitamins, such as vitamins A and D.

Key points

* Esters are formed by the reaction of an alcohol and a carboxylic acid.
* Forming an ester is an example of a condensation reaction as water is formed.
* Breaking down an ester is an example of a hydrolysis reaction.
* The name of an ester comes from the alcohol and carboxylic acid from which it is formed. For example, reacting ethanol and methanoic acid produces the ester ethyl methanoate.
* Esters are used as scents and solvents.
* Fats and oils are examples of esters.
* Fats and oils are formed from the reaction of glycerol with three fatty acids.
* Glycerol is an alcohol with three −OH groups.
* Fatty acids are carboxylic acids that contain a large number of carbon atoms.
* Fat molecules are mainly saturated and can pack closely together making them solid at room temperature.
* Oil molecules have a large number of double bonds and cannot pack closely together, making them liquids at room temperature.

Study questions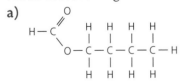

1 Draw full chemical structures for the following esters:
   a) methyl butanoate
   b) ethyl propanoate
   c) methyl ethanoate.

2 Draw the structures of
   a) the alcohol group
   b) the carboxyl group
   c) the ester link.

3 Name the following esters.
   a)

   Figure 5.13

   b)
   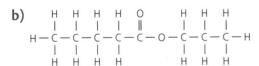

   Figure 5.14

4 Name the products formed when the esters in Question 1 are hydrolysed.

5 Name the type of reaction:
   a) when an alcohol reacts with a carboxylic acid to form an ester
   b) when an ester reacts with water to form an alcohol and a carboxylic acid.

6 Which of the following is a structural formula for glycerol?

A	B	C	D
CH$_2$OH	CH$_2$OH	CH$_2$OH	CH$_2$OH
|	|	|	|
CHOH	CH$_2$	CH$_2$OH	CHOH
|	|		|
CH$_2$OH	CH$_2$OH		CH$_2$COOH

7 Fats have higher melting points than oils because, when comparing fats and oils,

A fats have more hydrogen bonds
B fat molecules are more saturated
C fat molecules are more loosely packed
D fats have stronger covalent bonds.

8 Vitamins can be classed as being 'fat soluble' or 'water soluble'. The structures of vitamin C, a water-soluble vitamin, and vitamin A, a fat-soluble vitamin, are shown in Figures 5.15 and 5.16.

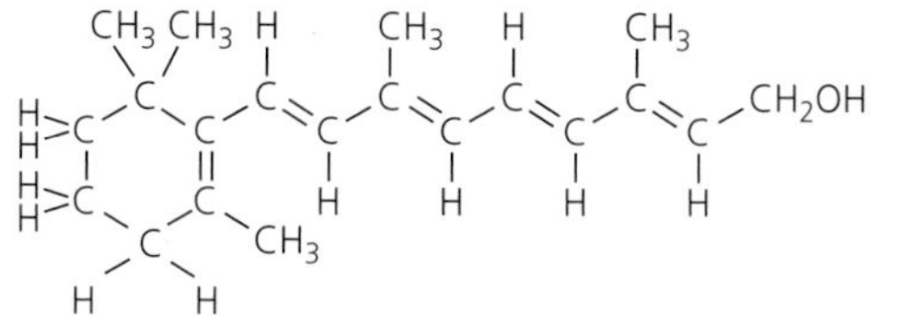

Figure 5.15 Vitamin A, fat soluble

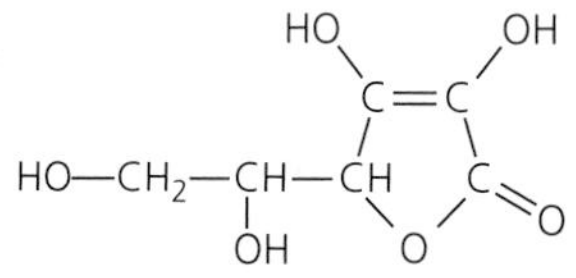

Figure 5.16 Vitamin C, water soluble

a) In terms of structure, why is vitamin C a water-soluble vitamin?
b) In terms of structure, why is vitamin A a fat-soluble vitamin?

9 Explain why oil molecules have lower melting points than fat molecules.

10 a) Explain why the molecule shown as Figure 5.17 is known as a monoglyceride.

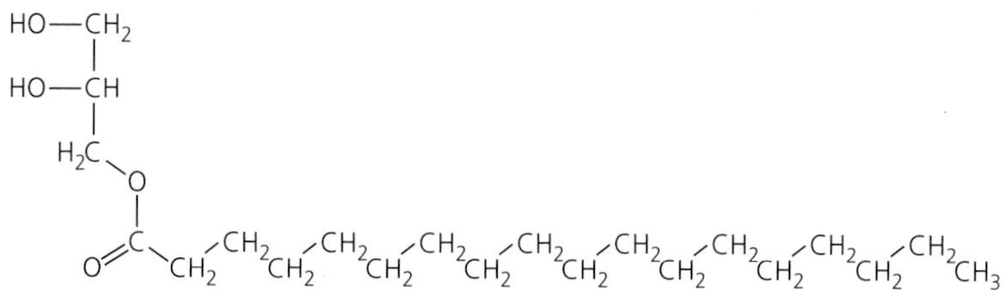

Figure 5.17

b) Which part of the monoglyceride could dissolve in a non-polar solvent such as hexane?

Chapter 6
Proteins

Proteins are nitrogen-containing compounds with many functions in the human body, as shown in Table 6.1.

Table 6.1 Examples of proteins and their functions

Name of protein	Where found	Function
Collagen	Tendons, muscle and bone	Gives structural support
Keratin	Hair, skin and nails	Gives structural support
Myosin	Muscles	Helps muscles to contract
Insulin	Pancreas	Hormone which helps to control blood glucose levels
Haemoglobin	Red blood cells	Transports oxygen around the body
Immunoglobulins	Blood, tears, saliva, skin	Fight infection
Amylase	Saliva and pancreas	An enzyme which breaks down starch

Enzymes – sometimes described as biological catalysts – are examples of proteins. The specific shape of a protein allows it to catalyse a specific reaction.

All proteins are made up of smaller molecules known as **amino acids**. Amino acids contain an **amine** group ($-NH_2$) and a carboxyl group ($-COOH$). Figure 6.1 shows the typical structure of an amino acid. Figure 6.2 shows the structures of six common amino acids.

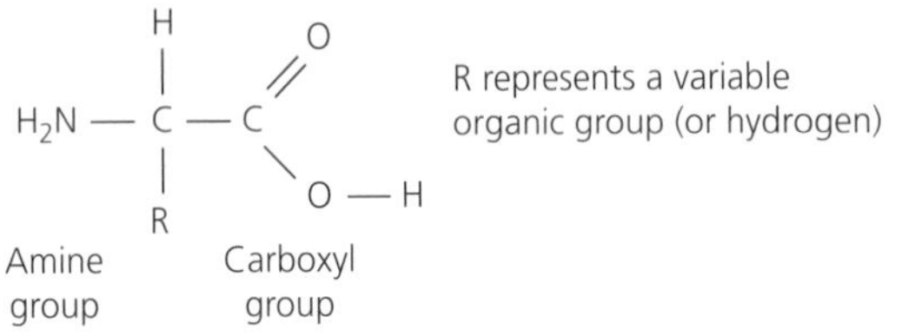

Figure 6.1 Amino acid structure

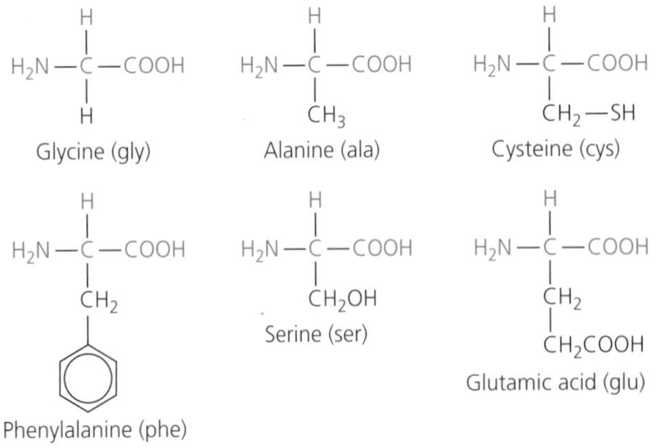

Figure 6.2 The structures of six common amino acids

Making a protein

Several amino acid molecules react together to form a protein molecule. This reaction involves the amine group reacting with the carboxyl group to form an **amide link**. Water is formed when this reaction takes place. As amino acids are joined by elimination of water, the *reaction* of amino acids to form a protein is an example of a condensation reaction. This is illustrated in Figure 6.3. Note that the amide link is also known as the **peptide link**.

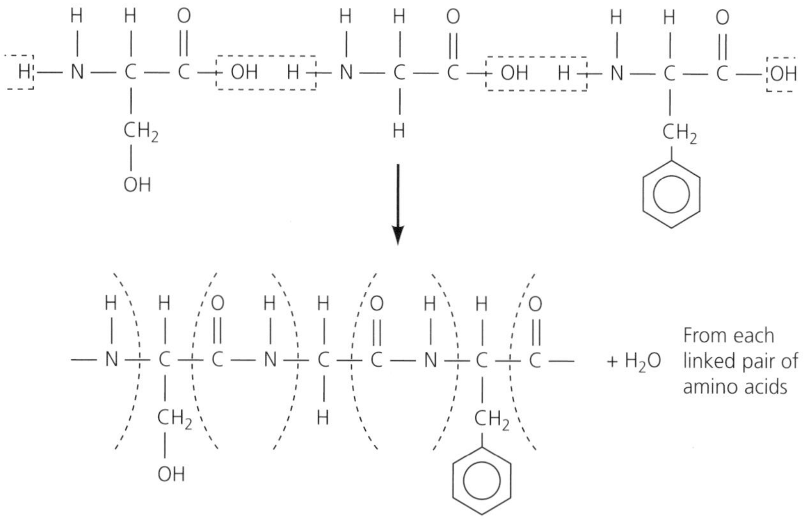

Figure 6.3 Condensation reaction of amino acids to form a protein. The amide links are shown in brackets.

Breaking a protein

The order in which amino acids join together determines the type of protein formed. The human body requires a source of amino acids in order to make the proteins needed to maintain and regulate life. Fortunately, the human body can make most of its own amino acids. There are, however, several amino acids which the body cannot make: these are known as **essential amino acids** and must be obtained from the diet.

Once eaten, proteins are broken down by the process of digestion to form the amino acids that make up the protein. This process is known as **hydrolysis** and is shown in Figure 6.4.

Both amino acids and proteins contain an N–H bond. This is significant as it allows hydrogen bonding to take place. Hydrogen bonding between protein molecules allows long protein strands to curl into different shapes. Heating a protein causes some, or all, of the hydrogen bonds to break, leading to a change of shape. This happens when an enzyme is heated; we say that heating the enzyme causes it to **denature**. In other words, the breaking of the hydrogen bonds results in a change of shape.

Hints & tips

You should be able to draw and recognise the functional groups mentioned in this chapter: amine, carboxyl and amide/peptide.

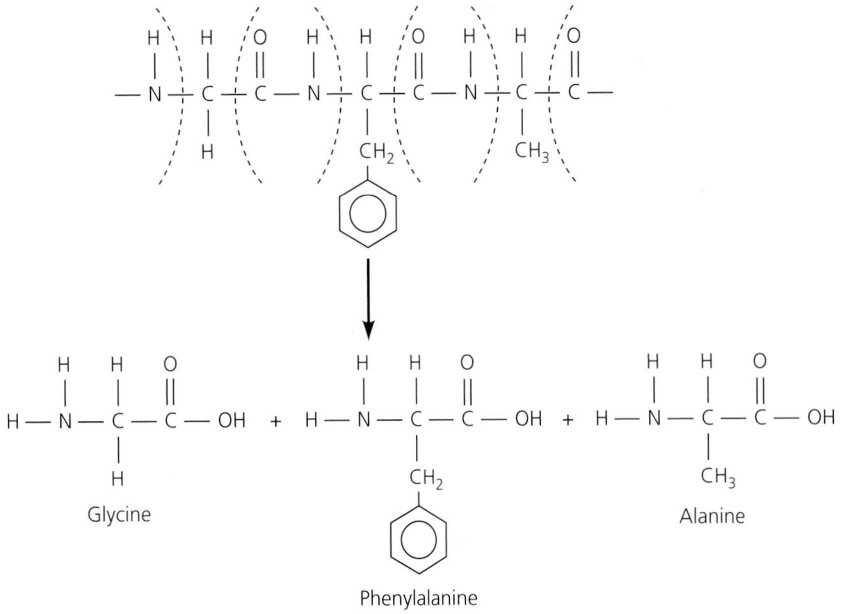

Figure 6.4 Hydrolysis of a protein to form amino acids

Key points !

* Amino acids are small molecules that contain an amine group ($-NH_2$) and a carboxyl group ($-COOH$).
* An amino acid can react with a neighbouring amino acid by reacting an amine group with a carboxyl group. The resultant bond formed is known as an amide (or peptide) link.
* When amino acids react together, water is eliminated. This is a condensation reaction.
* The splitting up of a protein into amino acids is known as a hydrolysis reaction.
* Essential amino acids are those amino acids required by the body which cannot be made by the body; they must be obtained from the diet.

Study questions ?

1 Which of the following represents an amino acid?
   A CH_3NH_2
   B C_6H_5COOH
   C H_2NCH_2COOH
   D $NCCH_3COOH$

2 Which of the following statements correctly describes an essential amino acid?
   A An amino acid that can only be made by the body.
   B An amino acid that must be obtained from the diet.
   C An amino acid that performs a key function in the body.
   D An amino acid that is only found in one type of protein.

3 A tripeptide X has the structure shown in Figure 6.5. Partial hydrolysis of X yields a mixture of dipeptides. Which of the dipeptides shown in Figure 6.6 could be produced on hydrolysing X?

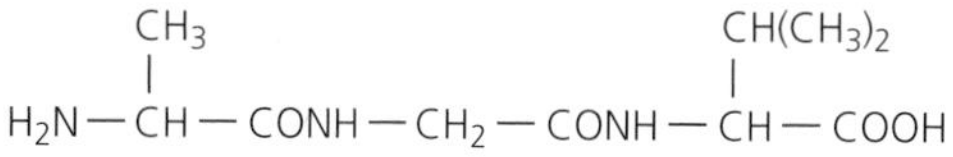

$$
\begin{array}{cccc}
CH_3 & & CH(CH_3)_2 \\
| & & | \\
H_2N-CH-CONH-CH_2-CONH-CH-COOH
\end{array}
$$

Figure 6.5

A
$$
\begin{array}{cc}
& CH_3 \\
& | \\
H_2N-CH_2-CONH-CH-COOH
\end{array}
$$

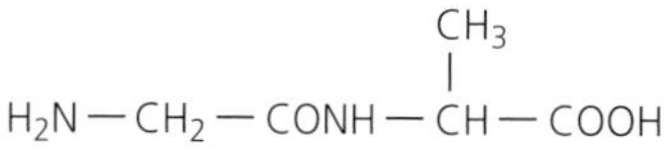

B
$$
\begin{array}{cc}
CH_3 & CH(CH_3)_2 \\
| & | \\
H_2N-CH-CONH-CH-COOH
\end{array}
$$

C
$$
\begin{array}{c}
CH(CH_3)_2 \\
| \\
H_2N-CH-CONH-CH_2-COOH
\end{array}
$$

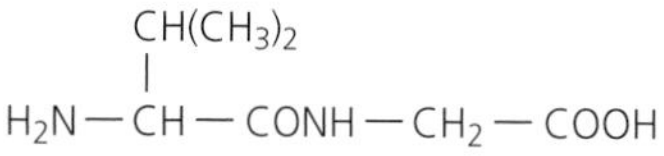

D
$$
\begin{array}{c}
CH(CH_3)_2 \\
| \\
H_2N-CH_2-CONH-CH-COOH
\end{array}
$$

Figure 6.6

4 Some amino acids are called α-amino acids because the amino group is on the carbon atom next to the acid group. Which of the following is an α-amino acid?

A
$$
\begin{array}{c}
CH_3-CH-COOH \\
| \\
CH_2-NH_2
\end{array}
$$

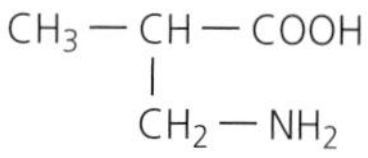

B
$$
\begin{array}{cc}
CH_2-CH-COOH \\
| \quad | \\
SH \quad NH_2
\end{array}
$$

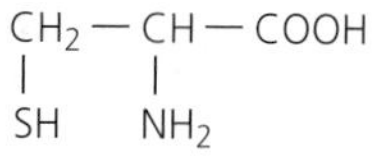

C

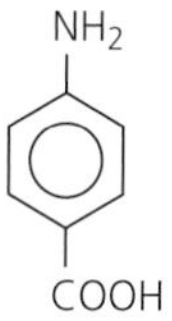

D

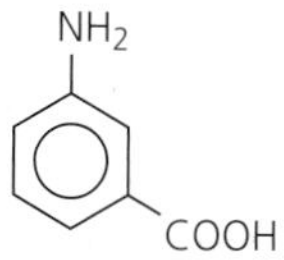

Figure 6.7

5 When two amino acids condense together, water is eliminated and a peptide link is formed. Which of the following represents this process?

A

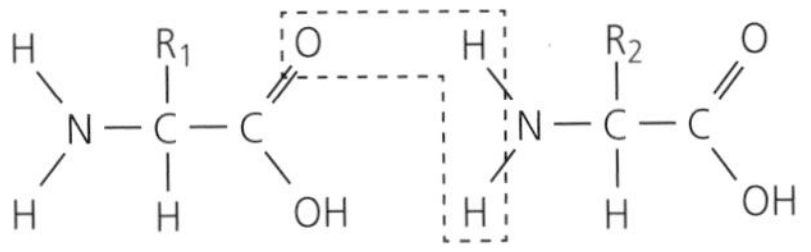

B

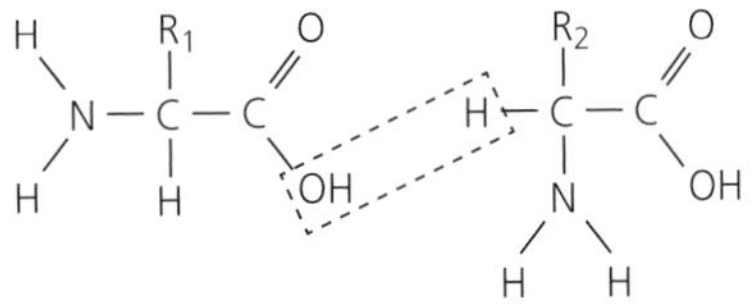

C

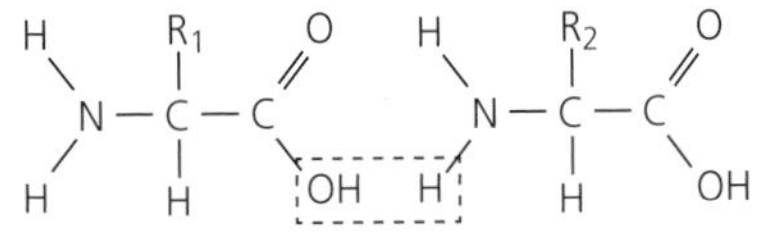

D

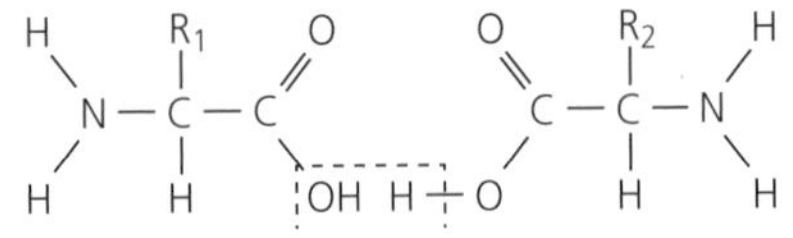

Figure 6.8

6 Phenylalanine and alanine can react to form the dipeptide shown.
   a) On a copy of the dipeptide, circle the peptide link in the molecule.
   b) Draw a structural formula for the other dipeptide that can be formed from phenylalanine and alanine.

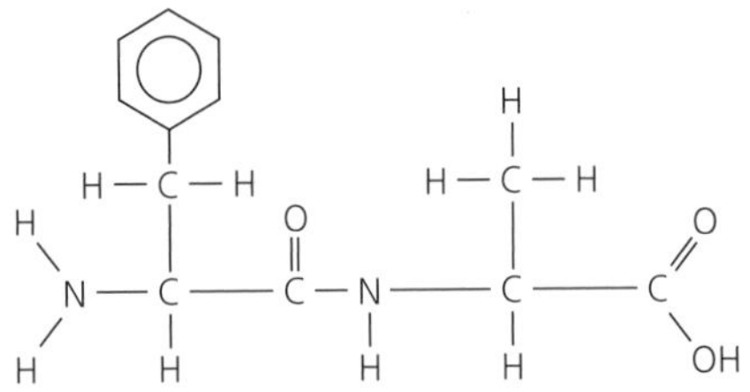

Figure 6.9

Chapter 7
Oxidation and the chemistry of cooking

Alcohols

Alcohols are carbon compounds that contain the hydroxyl functional group, −OH. The names of some straight-chain alcohols are shown in Table 7.1.

Table 7.1 Naming straight-chain alcohols

Alkanes	Alcohols
Methane CH_4	Methanol CH_3OH
Ethane C_2H_6	Ethanol C_2H_5OH
Propane C_3H_8	Propanol C_3H_7OH
Butane C_4H_{10}	Butanol C_4H_9OH
Pentane C_5H_{12}	Pentanol $C_5H_{11}OH$
Hexane C_6H_{14}	Hexanol $C_6H_{13}OH$
Heptane C_7H_{16}	Heptanol $C_7H_{15}OH$
Octane C_8H_{18}	Octanol $C_8H_{17}OH$
General formula: C_nH_{2n+2}	General formula: $C_nH_{2n+1}OH$ or $C_nH_{2n+2}O$

Alcohols are named by:
- numbering from the side which gives the −OH the lowest number
- ensuring the −OH takes priority over any branches.

The alcohol shown in Figure 7.1 would be called 3-methylbutan-1-ol.

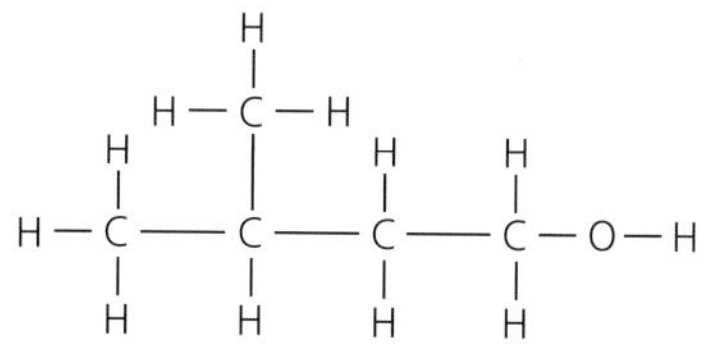

Figure 7.1 Systematic naming of alcohols

In the case of the alcohol in Figure 7.1, numbering of the carbon atoms starts from the right-hand side of the molecule to give the lowest number to the −OH. This places the methyl branch on position 3.

Alcohols can be subdivided into three different types depending on the position of the hydroxyl group. These are summarised in Table 7.2.

Table 7.2 Classification of alcohols

Type	Primary	Secondary	Tertiary
Position of −OH group	Joined to the *end* of the carbon chain	Joined to an *intermediate* carbon atom	Joined to an *intermediate* carbon atom which also has a branch attached

Characteristic group of atoms	$-CH_2OH$	— CH —
		    |
		    OH
			|
			— C —
			   |
			   OH

Table 7.3 shows the systematic names and classification of some alcohols.

Table 7.3 Naming alcohols

Structure	Name	Classification
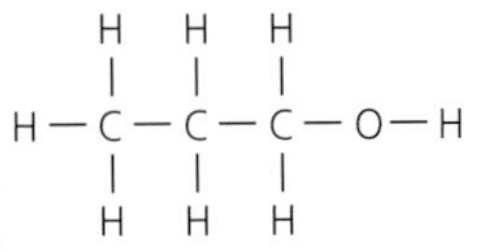	Propan-1-ol	Primary
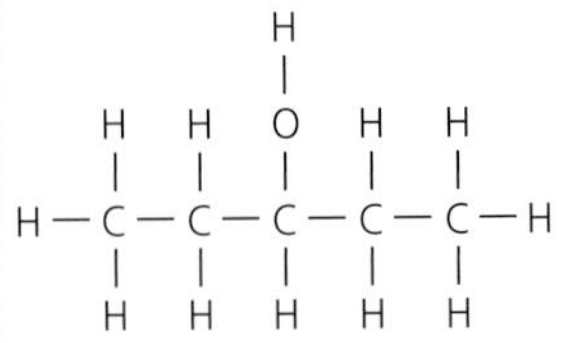	Pentan-3-ol	Secondary
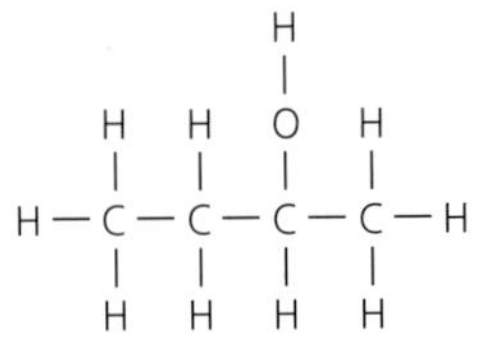	Butan-2-ol	Secondary
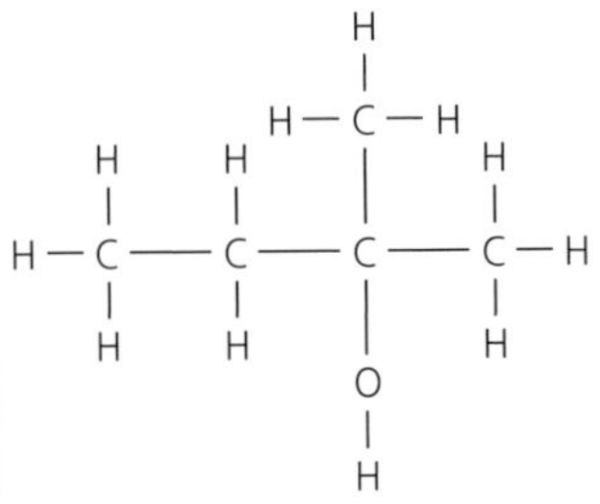	2-Methylbutan-2-ol	Tertiary
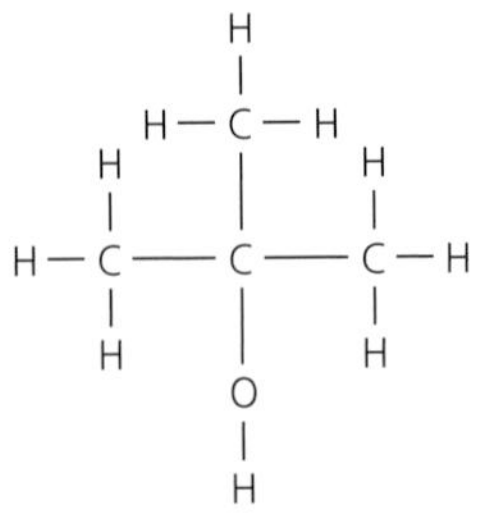	2-Methylpropan-2-ol	Tertiary

Alcohols and hydrogen bonding

An examination of the structures shown in Table 7.4 illustrates the effect of hydrogen bonding. Propane, which does not have a hydroxyl group, cannot form a hydrogen bond with other propane molecules. Consequently, propane has a much lower boiling point than the other molecules as only weak London dispersion forces have to be broken to change propane from a liquid to a gas. Adding hydroxyl groups has a significant effect on the boiling point as the molecules are held together by hydrogen bonding in the solid and liquid state. Much more energy must be supplied to overcome the hydrogen bonds which attract the molecules. Now compare the alcohols: as the number of −OH groups increases, more hydrogen bonds can be formed between molecules. Therefore, the boiling point increases as more energy is required to break the hydrogen bonds.

Table 7.4 Alcohols and hydrogen bonding

Name of compound	Structure	Boiling point/°C
Propane	H H H │ │ │ H—C—C—C—H │ │ │ H H H	−42
Propan-1-ol	H H H │ │ │ H—C—C—C—O—H │ │ │ H H H	97
Propan-1,2-diol	H H H │ │ │ H—C—C—C—H │ │ │ H OH OH	188
Propane-1,2,3-triol (Glycerol)	H H H │ │ │ H—C—C—C—H │ │ │ OH OH OH	290

Oxidation of alcohols

Primary and secondary alcohols can be oxidised by various oxidising agents but tertiary alcohols do not undergo **oxidation** readily. Suitable oxidising agents are *acidified potassium dichromate* and *hot copper (II) oxide*.

Remember

- When primary alcohols are oxidised they produce **aldehydes**.
- When secondary alcohols are oxidised they produce **ketones**.

The following tables show the structures of aldehydes and ketones and their parent alcohols.

Table 7.5 Oxidation of ethanol produces ethanal.

Alcohol	Aldehyde
Ethanol	Ethanal
CH_3CH_2OH	CH_3CHO
H H │ │ H—C—C—OH │ │ H H	H O │ ∥ H—C—C │ ＼ H H
The structure of ethanol	The structure of ethanal

Table 7.6 Oxidation of propan-1-ol produces propanal.

Alcohol	Aldehyde
Propan-1-ol	Propanal
$CH_3CH_2CH_2OH$	CH_3CH_2CHO
The structure of propan-1-ol	The structure of propanal

Table 7.7 Oxidation of propan-2-ol produces propanone.

Alcohol	Ketone
Propan-2-ol	Propanone
$CH_3CH(OH)CH_3$	CH_3COCH_3
The structure of propan-2-ol	The structure of propanone

Table 7.8 Oxidation of butan-2-ol produces butanone.

Alcohol	Ketone
Butan-2-ol	Butanone
$CH_3CH_2CH(OH)CH_3$	$CH_3CH_2COCH_3$
The structure of butan-2-ol	The structure of butanone

Aldehydes and ketones can be identified by the presence of the carbon–oxygen double bond, C=O, which is known as the **carbonyl group**. In an aldehyde, the carbonyl group is at the end of the carbon chain and has a hydrogen atom attached to it. In a ketone, the carbonyl group is joined to two other carbon atoms and does not have a hydrogen atom attached to it.

Branched aldehydes and ketones are named by giving priority to the carbonyl functional group.

Examples are shown in Table 7.9.

Table 7.9 Naming aldehydes and ketones

Structure	Name	Aldehyde or ketone
(structure diagram)	2-Methylpropanal	Aldehyde
(structure diagram)	4-Methylpentanal	Aldehyde
(structure diagram)	4-Methyloctan-3-one	Ketone
(structure diagram)	2,4-Dimethylhexan-3-one	Ketone

Hints & tips ⭐

There is no need to indicate a number for the functional group when naming an aldehyde as the carbonyl group is always at the end of the carbon chain. However, when naming a ketone, it is usually necessary to specify the number of the carbonyl group.

Oxidation of aldehydes

Oxidising agents can be used to distinguish between aldehydes and ketones since aldehydes can oxidise but ketones cannot. The three most common oxidising agents used are *Fehling's solution, Tollen's reagent* and *acidified potassium dichromate.*

Table 7.10 Oxidising agents

Oxidising agent	Observations	Explanation
Acidified potassium dichromate solution	Orange → green	$Cr_2O_7^{2-}(aq)$ reduced to $Cr^{3+}(aq)$
Fehling's solution	Blue → orange/red	$Cu^{2+}(aq)$ reduced to $Cu_2O(s)$ i.e. $Cu^{2+} + e^- \rightarrow Cu^+$
Tollen's reagent	Colourless → silver	$Ag^+(aq)$ reduced to $Ag(s)$ i.e. $Ag^+ + e^- \rightarrow Ag$

When oxidised, aldehydes form carboxylic acids, as shown in Tables 7.11 and 7.12.

Table 7.11 Oxidation of ethanal produces ethanoic acid.

Aldehyde	Carboxylic acid
Ethanal	Ethanoic acid
CH_3CHO	CH_3COOH
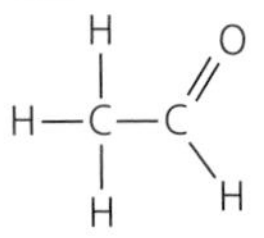 The structure of ethanal	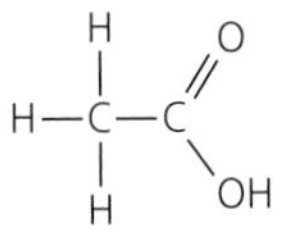 The structure of ethanoic acid

Table 7.12 Oxidation of butanal produces butanoic acid.

Aldehyde	Carboxylic acid
Butanal	Butanoic acid
$CH_3CH_2CH_2CHO$	$CH_3 CH_2CH_2COOH$
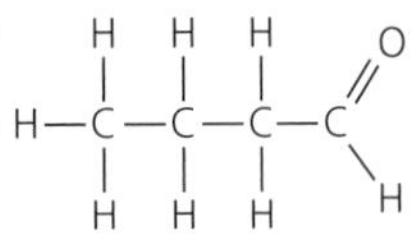 The structure of butanal	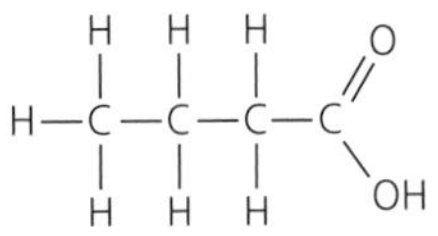 The structure of butanoic acid

Carboxylic acids contain the carboxyl functional group (–COOH).

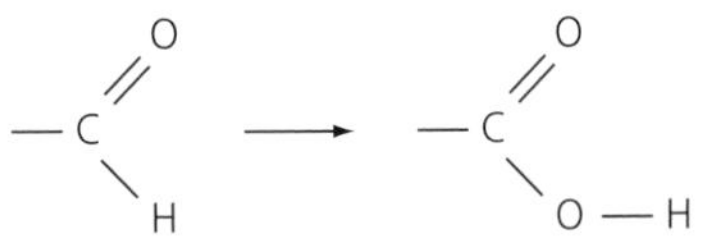

Figure 7.2 Oxidation of an aldehyde produces a carboxylic acid.

Hints & tips

The oxidation of alcohols can be summarised as follows:

1 Primary alcohol → Aldehyde → Carboxylic acid
2 Secondary alcohol → Ketone (not readily oxidised)
3 Tertiary alcohol (not readily oxidised)

Oxidation and the oxygen to hydrogen ratio

When dealing with carbon compounds, a useful method for determining whether oxidation or reduction has occurred involves calculating the oxygen to hydrogen ratio. This is illustrated in Table 7.13, which shows the oxidation of ethanol to form ethanal and then ethanoic acid.

Table 7.13 Oxidation and the O:H ratio

Primary alcohol	Aldehyde	Carboxylic acid
Ethanol	Ethanal	Ethanoic acid
CH_3CH_2OH	CH_3CHO	CH_3COOH
O:H ratio 1:6	O:H ratio 1:4	O:H ratio 1:2

We can use the oxygen to hydrogen ratio to show that:

- oxidation occurs when there is an increase in the oxygen to hydrogen ratio
- reduction occurs when there is a decrease in the oxygen to hydrogen ratio.

Naming carboxylic acids

Branched carboxylic acids are named by giving priority to the carboxyl group. Examples are shown in Table 7.14.

Table 7.14 Naming branched chain carboxylic acids

Structure	Molecular formula	Name
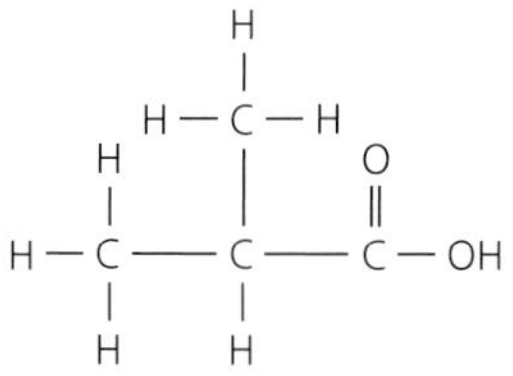	$C_4H_8O_2$	2-Methylpropanoic acid
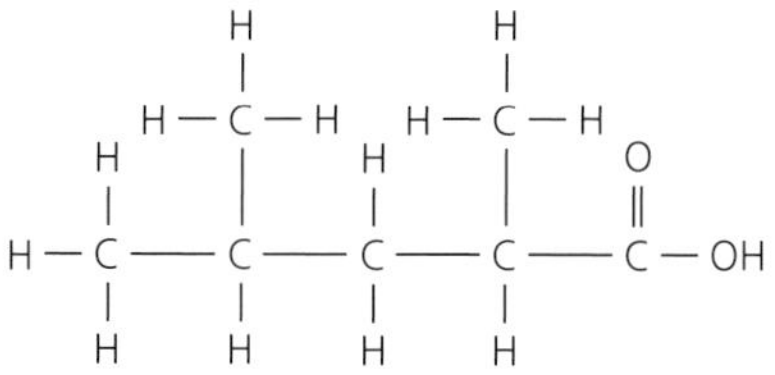	$C_7H_{14}O_2$	2,4-Dimethylpentanoic acid
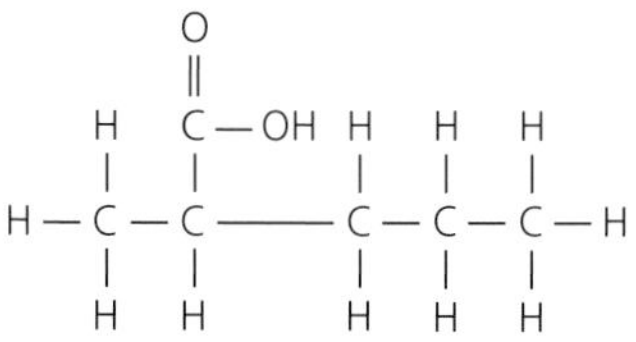	$C_6H_{12}O_2$	2-Methylpentanoic acid

Reactions of carboxylic acids

Reduction

Carboxylic acids are produced from the oxidation of primary alcohols and aldehydes. The reverse of this reaction can be used to produce primary alcohols and aldehydes. In other words, carboxylic acids can undergo **reduction**. This is illustrated in Figure 7.3.

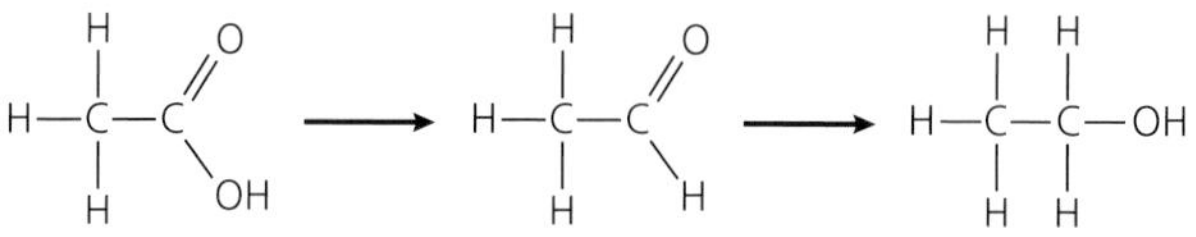

Figure 7.3 Reduction of ethanoic acid

Key points

* Alcohols can be classed as primary, secondary or tertiary.
* As they contain the hydroxyl group (−OH), alcohols can hydrogen bond. This accounts for alcohols having higher boiling points when compared to alkanes.
* Alcohols are soluble in water as they contain the polar hydroxyl group.
* Primary and secondary alcohols can be oxidised to form aldehydes and ketones using oxidising agents such as acidified potassium dichromate or hot copper (II) oxide.
* Tertiary alcohols cannot be oxidised using mild oxidising agents.
* Aldehydes and ketones contain the carbonyl group (−C=O).
* Aldehydes can be oxidised further to produce carboxylic acids using acidified potassium dichromate, Fehling's solution or Tollen's reagent; ketones cannot be oxidised.
* Carboxylic acids can be reduced to form aldehydes or primary alcohols.
* Carboxylic acids can react with bases to form salts.
* Oxidation involves an increase in the O:H ratio.
* Flavour and aroma molecules in food are often aldehydes and ketones. Oxidation of these molecules can change the flavour, making foods taste unpleasant, so antioxidants are used to prevent this oxidation and thus preserve flavour.
* The chemical structure of a food molecule can be used to determine whether the molecule is likely to be soluble or insoluble in water or oil. The volatility of a flavour compound is also determined by its structure.
* Heating protein molecules results in the protein changing shape. This is known as denaturing.

Study questions

Questions 1–5 refer to the molecules shown in Table 7.16.

Table 7.16

A	B	C
H–C–C–C–H with OH	H–C–C–C–C–H with O	H–C–C–C with O, O–H
D	E	F
H–C–C–C–O–H	H–C–C–C–C with O, O–H	H–C–C–C–C with O, H

1 Identify the compound which can be oxidised to form the compound shown in box C.

2 Identify the compound which can be formed when the compound shown in box E is reduced.

3 Identify the secondary alcohol.

4 Identify the ketone.

5 Which two compounds could react with NaOH(aq) to form a salt?

6 Compound X reacted with hot copper (II) oxide and the organic product did not give a colour change when heated with Fehling's solution. Compound X could be

A butan-1-ol

B butan-2-ol

C butanone

D butanoic acid.

7 Vanillin and eugenol are examples of small molecules which are responsible for the flavour in food. Their structures are shown in Figures 7.7 and 7.8. With reference to the structures, explain why vanillin is more soluble in water than eugenol.

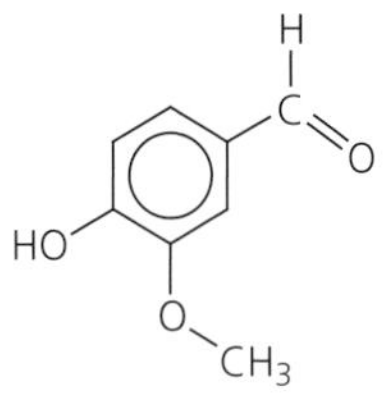

Figure 7.7 Vanillin

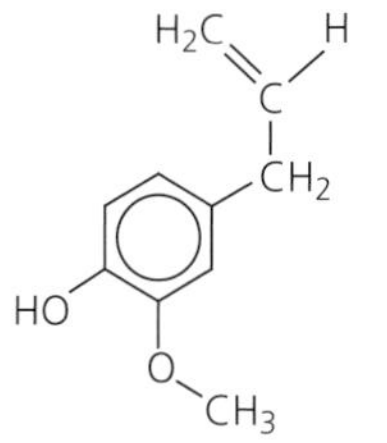

Figure 7.8 Eugenol

8 Collagen is a protein found in animals which helps attach muscles to the bone. Heating meat which contains collagen results in the flavour of the meat changing.

a) With reference to collagen, explain why heating meat results in the flavour changing.

b) Boiling meat for several hours can also result in some of the collagen hydrolysing. Name the type of compounds formed when collagen is hydrolysed.

9 Name the following carboxylic acids.

a)

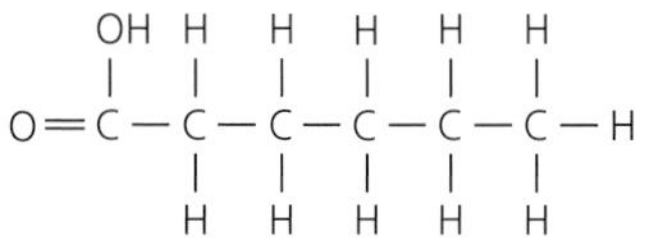

b)

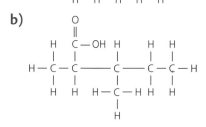

Figure 7.9

10 a) Draw the structures of butan-1-ol and butan-1,3-diol.

b) Explain why butan-1,3-diol has a higher boiling point than butan-1-ol.

Chapter 8
Soaps, detergents and emulsions

Fats and oils are examples of esters. When they hydrolyse, they produce glycerol and carboxylic acids known as fatty acids. If the hydrolysis is carried out using an alkali such as NaOH(aq), the fatty acids immediately react to form salts. This is illustrated by the reaction shown in Figure 8.1. These salts are what we commonly refer to as soaps.

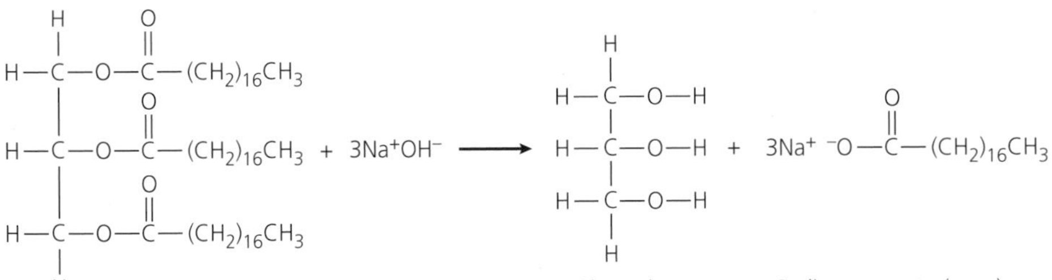

Figure 8.1 Alkaline hydrolysis of a fat produces glycerol and soap.

The structure and cleansing mechanism of soap

Fats and oils are the main compounds found in greasy stains from foods. Since fats and oils are non-polar compounds, they will not readily dissolve in water. Instead, a soap is required to help dissolve the greasy stain and remove it from clothes or skin.

As shown in Figure 8.1, a soap is the salt of a carboxylic acid. Since the carboxylic acids found in fats and oils have long hydrocarbon chains, soap molecules also contain long, non-polar hydrocarbon chains. In addition, soaps contain a carboxylate 'head' formed from the reaction of the carboxyl group (–COOH) with the base. Overall, soaps are said to have a polar head and a non-polar tail. This is represented in Figures 8.2 and 8.3.

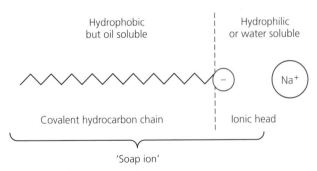

Figure 8.2 The structure of a soap

$$CH_3(CH_2)_{14}COO^-$$

Hydrophobic tail   Hydrophilic head
Figure 8.3 A soap ion

The hydrocarbon tail can bond easily to greasy stains on clothes or skin. This part of the soap molecule does not dissolve in water; it is **hydrophobic**. The ionic head does dissolve in water; it is **hydrophilic**. As shown in Figure 8.4, the soap molecules can dissolve in the grease causing it to be covered in negative charge. The negative charges repel resulting in the grease breaking up into globules which are attracted to water allowing them to be washed away when water is added.

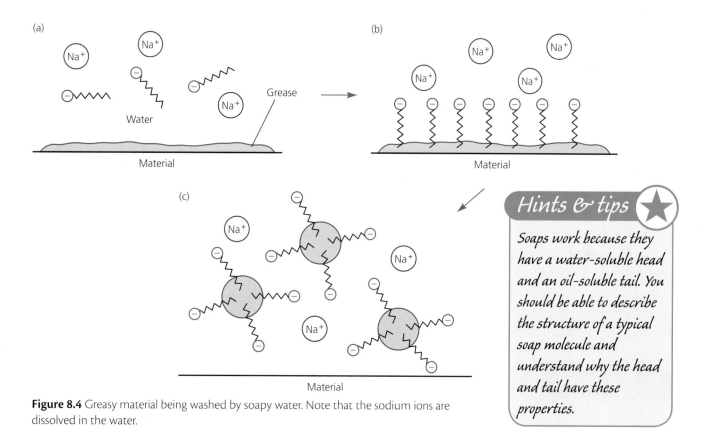

Figure 8.4 Greasy material being washed by soapy water. Note that the sodium ions are dissolved in the water.

Hints & tips

Soaps work because they have a water-soluble head and an oil-soluble tail. You should be able to describe the structure of a typical soap molecule and understand why the head and tail have these properties.

Detergents

Detergents are compounds with a soap-like structure which allows them to remove greasy stains. They have a non-polar tail, which is oil soluble, and a polar head, which is water soluble. An example of a detergent molecule is dodecylbenzenesulfonate: $CH_3(CH_2)_{11}C_6H_4SO_3^-$.

The main difference in structure between a soap and a detergent is the head. The head part of a detergent will always be soluble in water. This can be achieved by using heads which are negative ions (such as the sulfonate ion), positive ions or have an overall polar structure. The detergent head will never, however, be formed from a carboxylate ion.

The water supply in many regions in the UK is known as 'hard water' as it is rich in dissolved calcium and magnesium ions. When this water is mixed with soap, instead of forming a soapy lather, a precipitate is formed:

$$CH_3(CH_2)_{14}COO^-(aq) + Ca^{2+}(aq) \rightarrow (CH_3(CH_2)_{14}COO)_2Ca(s)$$

This precipitate reduces the cleansing action of the soap and builds up to leave a 'scum' around baths, sinks and shower heads. Detergents do not form precipitates with calcium or magnesium ions as they do not contain the carboxylate ion. Hence, detergents are very useful in hard-water areas as an alternative to soap.

Emulsions and emulsifiers

An **emulsion** is a liquid which contains small droplets of another liquid, such as soapy grease particles mixed in water. The grease and water would normally separate into two separate layers, but the soap acts as an **emulsifier** as it helps to bring the two substances together. Emulsions in food are very common. Milk is mostly water but it also contains lots of fats. If you look at a glass of milk, you do not see the separate layers as milk contains emulsifiers which help the fatty parts of milk remain dispersed throughout the water.

Mayonnaise is an example of an emulsion formed by mixing olive oil and vinegar. Normally, the olive oil and vinegar would not mix and two separate layers would form. However, mayonnaise also comprises egg yolk which contains the compound lecithin. Lecithin acts as an emulsifier as it contains a charged part (which is water soluble) and a large hydrocarbon tail (which is non-polar). The vinegar is attracted to the charged part of lecithin while the olive oil is attracted to the hydrocarbon part of lecithin.

Figure 8.5 Milk and mayonnaise are examples of emulsions.

Key points ❗

* Soaps are fatty acid salts formed from the alkaline hydrolysis of fats or oils.
* Soap molecules contain a non-polar tail and a polar head.
* Soaps can dissolve greasy/oily stains as the non-polar tail will dissolve in the grease, coating the outside of the stain with repulsive negative charges from the polar heads. This causes the stain to break down into water-soluble globules.
* Detergents are soap-like molecules which will not form scummy precipitates with hard water as they have different polar heads from soaps.
* Emulsifiers are used to keep water-soluble and oil-soluble compounds together. They are widely used in the food industry and can be recognised as they have a non-polar part and a polar part.

$$
\begin{array}{l}
CH_2-O-\overset{\overset{\displaystyle O}{\|}}{C}-(CH_2)_{14}CH_3 \\
| \\
CH-O-\overset{\overset{\displaystyle O}{\|}}{C}-(CH_2)_{14}CH_3 \\
| \\
CH_2-O-\overset{\overset{\displaystyle O}{\|}}{P}-O-CH_2CH_2\overset{+}{N}(CH_3)_3 \\
\quad\quad\quad | \\
\quad\quad\quad O^-
\end{array}
$$

Figure 8.6 Lecithin is found in egg yolk and acts as an emulsifier.

Study questions

1 Which of the following compounds could act as a soap?
   A Stearic acid
   B Glycerol
   C Sodium stearate
   D Propyl stearate

2 Detergents are useful replacements for soaps as they
   A do not dissolve in water
   B do not form precipitates with water
   C do not dissolve in oil
   D do not contain glycerol.

3 The following compound is an example of an emulsifier.

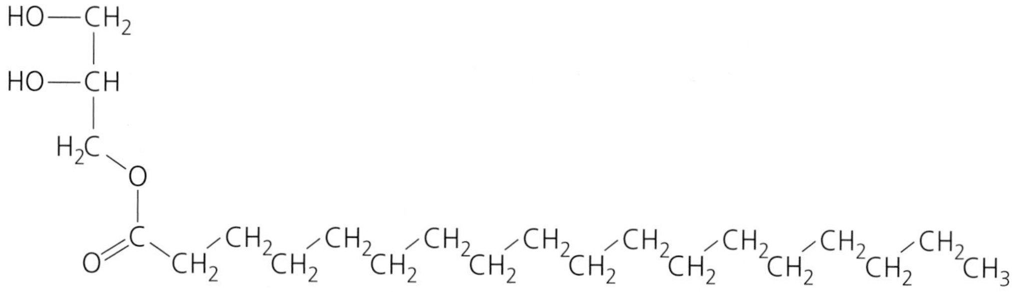

Figure 8.7

   a) Draw a structural formula for the alcohol formed when this compound is hydrolysed.
   b) Explain how this compound can act as an emulsifier.

4 A representation of the detergent molecule sodium dodecyl sulfate is shown in Figure 8.8.

Figure 8.8

   a) Part of the detergent molecule is circled. Suggest what this represents.
   b) Explain how a detergent molecule can dissolve an oily stain.

Chapter 9
Fragrances

Terpenes

Essential oils are concentrated extracts of the aroma compounds found in plants. These compounds are usually volatile and insoluble in water and can be found in almost any part of the plant. The family of compounds known as the **terpenes** are commonly found in essential oils.

Terpenes are compounds based on *isoprene* (2-methylbuta-1,3-diene), which has the molecular formula C_5H_8.

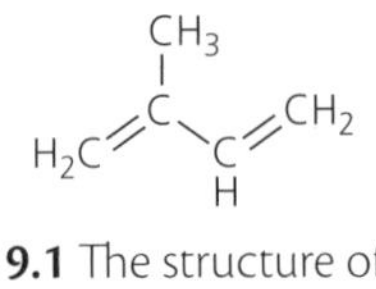

All terpenes contain isoprene units joined together. Terpene compounds can be given the formula $(C_5H_8)n$, where *n* is the number of terpene units joined together. For example, the terpene known as myrcene is formed from two isoprene units joined together, as shown in Figure 9.2.

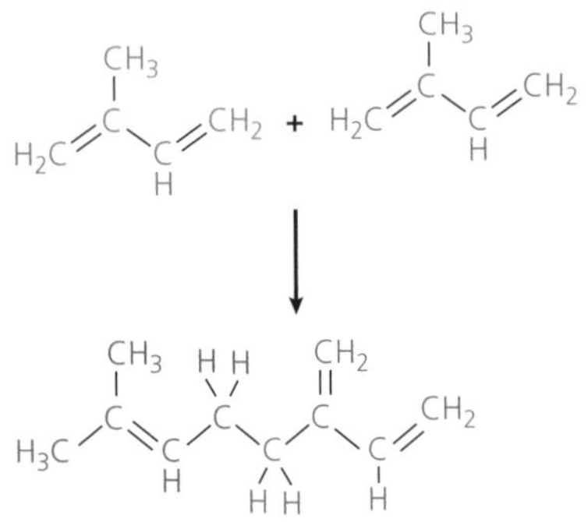

Figure 9.1 The structure of isoprene

Figure 9.2 Joining two isoprene units to form myrcene

Limonene, carvone and myrcene are all examples of terpenes formed from two isoprene units joining together.

Table 9.1 Examples of terpenes found in essential oils

Limonene	Carvone	Myrcene
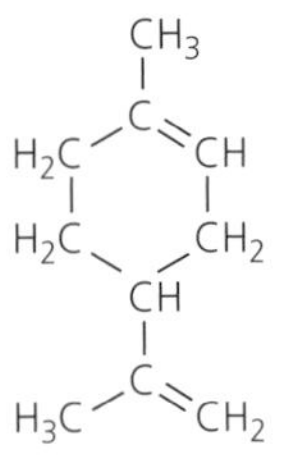 Citrus	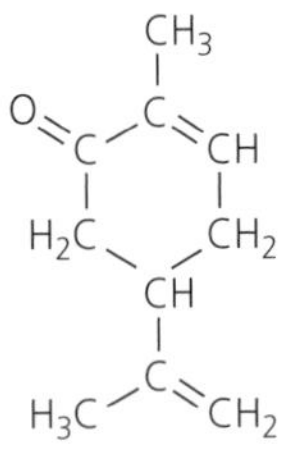 Spearmint	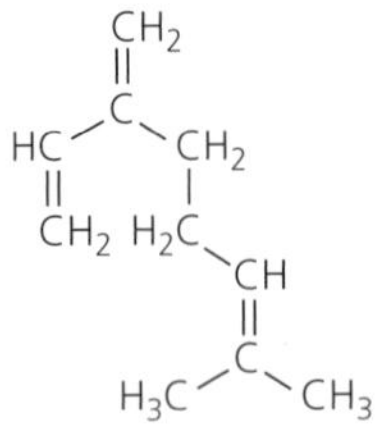 Woody smell

> ## Hints & tips
>
> *The number of terpene units used to form a terpene can be calculated by adding up the number of carbon atoms in the terpene and dividing this number by 5.*

Oxidation of terpenes

In nature, the oxidation of terpenes produces many of the compounds responsible for the aroma of spices derived from plants. For example, peppermint oil contains the terpene menthol and its oxidation product, menthone. Both compounds contribute to the flavour and aroma of the oil. An examination of the structures of menthol and menthone shows that the structural change is an example of a secondary alcohol (menthol) being oxidised to form a ketone (menthone).

Table 9.2 Oxidation of menthol produces menthone.

Terpene	Oxidised terpene	Where found?
Menthol 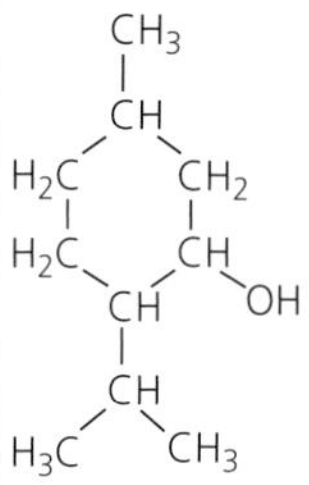	Menthone 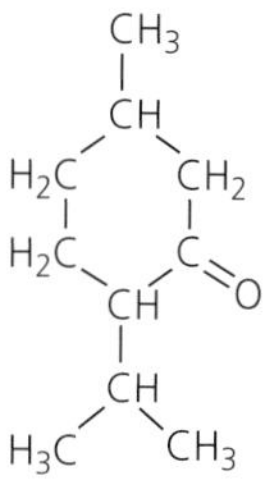	Peppermint oil 
CH₃ CH H₂C CH₂ H₂C CH CH OH CH H₃C CH₃	CH₃ CH H₂C CH₂ H₂C C CH O CH H₃C CH₃	

Key points !

* Essential oils are concentrated extracts of the aroma compounds found in plants.
* Terpenes are examples of compounds found in essential oils.
* Terpenes are compounds based on isoprene (2-methylbuta-1,3-diene).
* Oxidation of terpenes produces compounds that contribute to the flavour and aroma of spices derived from plants.

Study questions ?

1 Farnesol is a terpene found in the essential oil derived from a rose.

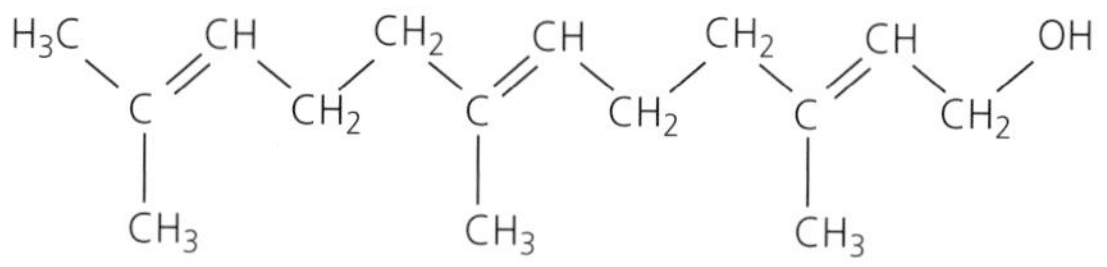

Figure 9.3

a) Terpenes are based on isoprene. Draw a structural formula for isoprene.

b) How many isoprene units must join to form farnesol?

2 Squalene is a terpene found in shark oil. Describe how a solution of bromine water could be used to distinguish between squalene and farnesol.

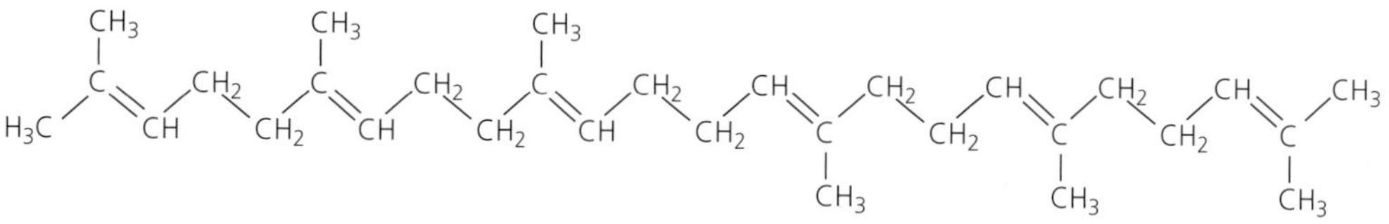

Figure 9.4

3 Citral (Figure 9.5) is a terpene oxidation product found in lemongrass. It is formed from the oxidation of nerol. Menthone (Figure 9.6) is a terpene oxidation product found in peppermint oil.

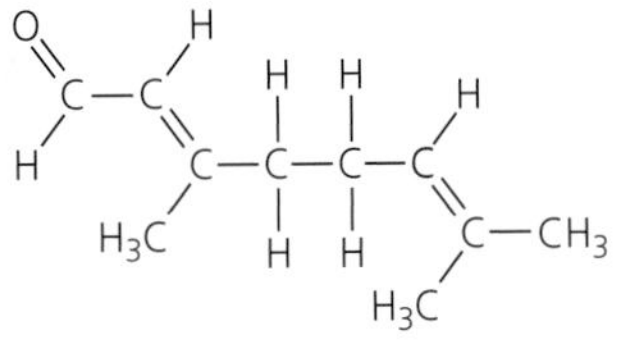

Figure 9.5 Citral

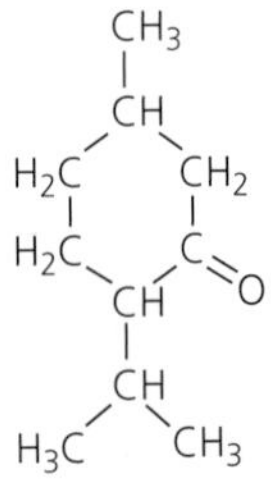

Figure 9.6 Menthone

a) Describe an experiment you could carry out that would allow you to distinguish between citral and menthone.

b) Draw a structural formula for the terpene nerol.

4 Erythrose (Figure 9.7) can be used in the production of a chewing gum that helps prevent tooth decay. Which of the compounds shown in Figure 9.8 will be the *best* solvent for erythrose?

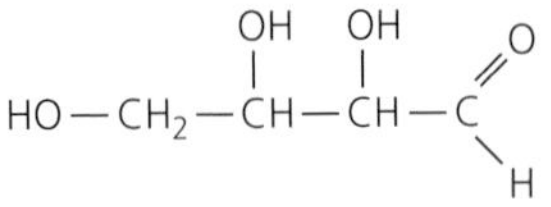

Figure 9.7 Erythrose

A

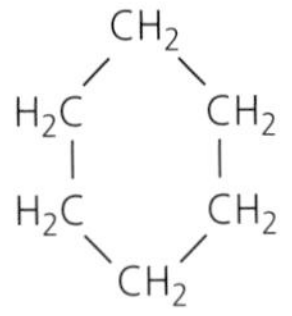

B $CH_3-CH_2-CH_2-CH_2-CH_2-CH_3$

C CH_3-CH_2-OH

D

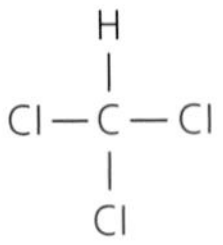

Figure 9.8

5 Limonene is one of the terpene molecules responsible for the flavour of lemons. How many isoprene units are used in the production of one limonene molecule?

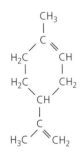

Figure 9.9 Limonene

A 1

B 2

C 3

D 4

6 Myrcene (Figure 9.10) is a simple terpene. Terpenes contain at least one isoprene unit. Which of the structures given in Figure 9.11 shows a correctly highlighted isoprene unit?

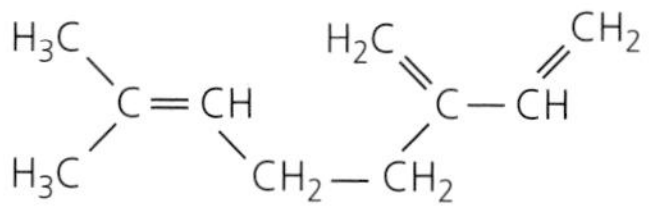

$$H_3C \diagdown C=CH \diagup CH_2-CH_2 \diagdown C-CH \diagup CH_2 \diagup$$

Figure 9.10 Myrcene

A, B, C, D

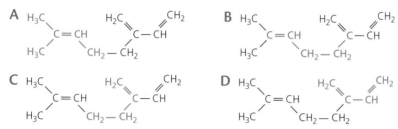

Figure 9.11

7 Two typical compounds that are present in many perfumes are shown.

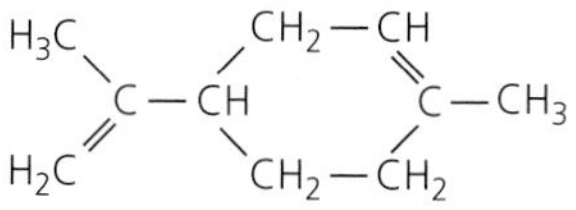

$C_{10}H_{16}$
Limonene

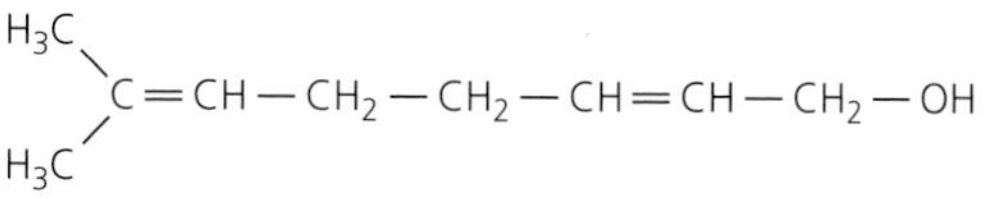

$C_9H_{16}O$
Geraniol

Figure 9.12

a) Why does geraniol evaporate more slowly than limonene?
b) The structure of one of the first synthetic scents used in perfume is shown below.

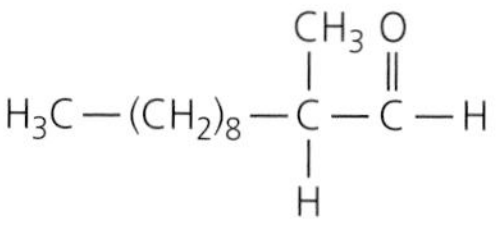

$$H_3C-(CH_2)_8-\overset{\overset{\displaystyle CH_3}{|}}{\underset{\underset{\displaystyle H}{|}}{C}}-\overset{\overset{\displaystyle O}{\|}}{C}-H$$

Figure 9.13

   i. Name the family of carbonyl compounds to which this synthetic scent belongs.
   ii. Copy and complete the structure below to show the product formed when this scent is oxidised.

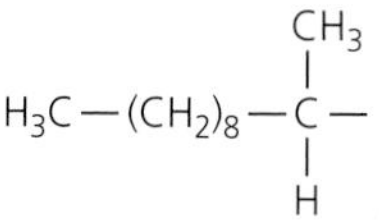

$$H_3C-(CH_2)_8-\overset{\overset{\displaystyle CH_3}{|}}{\underset{\underset{\displaystyle H}{|}}{C}}-$$

Figure 9.14

Ultraviolet light (UV)

Sunlight contains **ultraviolet light**, which is a very high energy light capable of breaking chemical bonds. Exposing our skin to UV light is beneficial as it allows us to make vitamin D, but it also causes our skin to age, and too much UV exposure can cause sunburn. As sunburn has been linked to skin cancer, chemists have developed products to protect our skin from the damaging effects of UV. *Sun screens* contain compounds that filter the UV light so that less UV reaches the skin. *Sunblock* contains compounds that reflect the UV so that it does not reach the skin at all.

Free radical reactions

UV light has enough energy to break covalent bonds leaving two atoms with unpaired electrons. For example, a chlorine molecule (Cl_2) contains two chlorine atoms bonded together by a covalent bond as shown in Figure 10.1.

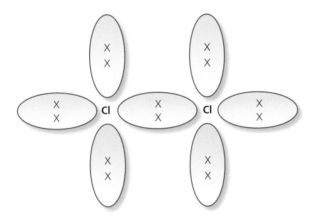

Figure 10.1 Two chlorine atoms joined by a covalent bond.

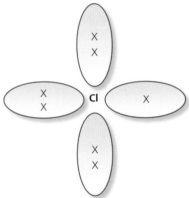

Figure 10.2 A chlorine free radical

When UV light is shone onto chlorine, the energy supplied causes the covalent bond to break to form two chlorine atoms. These atoms are highly reactive as they each have an unpaired electron. They are known as **free radicals**.

This chlorine atom is highly reactive as it has an unpaired electron. It will react rapidly with any other atom or molecule that comes into contact with it. Chemists have studied reactions involving free radicals and have observed a particular sequence of reactions. This is best illustrated by describing the reaction of methane, an alkane, with chlorine.

The overall reaction is:

$$CH_4 + Cl_2 \rightarrow CH_3Cl + HCl$$

This is known as a *substitution reaction* as one of the H atoms in the methane is substituted for a Cl atom. There are three steps to this reaction: *initiation, propagation* and *termination*.

Initiation

UV light is shone on a mixture of methane and chlorine. There is enough energy in the UV light to break the Cl–Cl bond to produce two Cl atoms.

$$Cl - Cl \rightarrow Cl^{\bullet} + Cl^{\bullet}$$

Propagation

The highly reactive chlorine radicals ($Cl^{\bullet}$) react with the methane molecules. This produces methyl radicals which then react with chlorine molecules (Cl_2).

$$Cl^{\bullet} + CH_4 \rightarrow CH_3^{\bullet} + HCl$$

$$CH_3^{\bullet} + Cl_2 \rightarrow CH_3Cl + Cl^{\bullet}$$

Termination

Two free radicals combine to form stable molecules.

$$Cl^{\bullet} + Cl^{\bullet} \rightarrow Cl_2$$

$$CH_3^{\bullet} + CH_3^{\bullet} \rightarrow C_2H_6$$

$$CH_3^{\bullet} + Cl^{\bullet} \rightarrow CH_3Cl$$

> ### Hints & tips ★
>
> *When writing the steps for a free radical reaction between a hydrocarbon and a halogen, remember that the initiation step always involves the halogen molecule breaking up to form two halogen radicals. The termination step is always the easiest: simply combine any two radicals to form a stable molecule.*

Example

Write initiation, propagation and termination steps for the reaction between bromine and propane.

Solution

Initiation:

$$Br - Br \rightarrow Br^{\bullet} + Br^{\bullet}$$

Propagation:

$$Br^{\bullet} + C_3H_8 \rightarrow C_3H_7^{\bullet} + HBr$$

$$C_3H_7^{\bullet} + Br_2 \rightarrow C_3H_7Br + Br^{\bullet}$$

Termination:

$$Br^{\bullet} + Br^{\bullet} \rightarrow Br_2$$

$$C_3H_7^{\bullet} + C_3H_7^{\bullet} \rightarrow C_6H_{14}$$

$$C_3H_7^{\bullet} + Br^{\bullet} \rightarrow C_3H_7Br$$

Free radical scavengers

Given that UV light can cause free radicals to form on our skin, which leads to ageing, cosmetic chemists have developed compounds that combine with these radicals to form stable molecules. These compounds are known as **free radical scavengers**. As they form stable molecules, they help to stop the free radical chain reactions that cause the skin to form wrinkles. Examples of free radical scavengers include vitamins C and E. Free radical scavengers are also added to food and plastics to prevent spoiling or damage by free radicals.

Key points !

* UV light is a high energy form of light that can break chemical bonds.
* Exposure to UV light causes ageing of the skin and can cause sunburn.
* Sunblocks stop UV light reaching the skin.
* Free radicals are highly reactive atoms or molecules with unpaired electrons.
* Free radicals can take part in chemical reactions that involve the steps initiation, propagation and termination.
* Free radical scavengers are molecules that react with free radicals to prevent chain reactions.
* Free radical scavengers are added to cosmetic products such as skin creams. They are also added to foods and plastics.

Study questions ?

1

A	B	C
$F_2 \rightarrow F^{\bullet} + F^{\bullet}$	$Cl^{\bullet} + Cl^{\bullet} \rightarrow Cl_2$	$CH_3^{\bullet} + Cl_2 \rightarrow CH_3Cl + Cl^{\bullet}$
D	E	F
$CH_3^{\bullet} + CH_3^{\bullet} \rightarrow C_2H_6$	$F_2 + H_2 \rightarrow 2HF$	$C_2H_4 + Br_2 \rightarrow C_2H_4Br_2$

a) Which box shows an initiation reaction?
b) Which two boxes show termination reactions?
c) Which box shows a propagation reaction?

2 Suncreams contain antioxidants. The antioxidant, compound A, can prevent damage to skin by reacting with free radicals such as $NO_2^{\bullet}$. Why can compound A be described as a free radical scavenger in the reaction shown below?

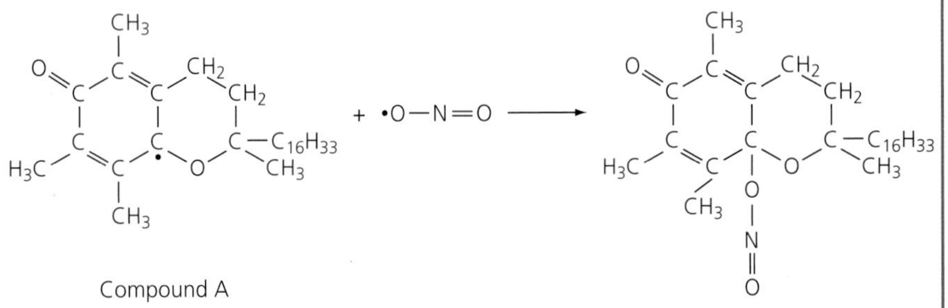

Compound A

Figure 10.3

Designing an industrial process

The chemical industry manufactures a huge variety of products including medicines, plastics, paints and cosmetics. As with any business, the chemical industry makes these products to generate a profit but it must consider how to make maximum profit while having minimal impact on people and the environment. Table 11.1 shows some of the factors that could influence the design of an industrial process and their effects on profits.

Environmental considerations

Every industry has a duty to protect the people who make its products, use its products and live nearby. The chemical industry has worked hard to promote a culture of health and safety and minimal impact on the environment.

Remember

The three main environmental considerations of the chemical industry are:

1 How can waste be minimised?
2 How can we avoid making toxic substances?
3 Can we design products that will biodegrade?

Once a product has been identified, chemists and engineers will work together to address these considerations. Sometimes this will involve attempting to make a new compound using an alternative route that does not generate so much waste or investigating new types of catalyst to make a reaction more efficient. Recycling of reactants is a common and obvious step taken to reduce waste in a chemical process.

Table 11.1 Factors affecting the design of a chemical process

Factor	Profit making	Profit losing
Availability, sustainability and cost of **feedstock**(s)	If the process relies on a feedstock which is available locally, this will help to keep costs down and maximise profit.	If the feedstock has to be transported from further afield, this will have significant cost, safety and environmental considerations. Is the feedstock likely to last for a long time or is it likely to become scarce? This could significantly affect the cost of buying the feedstock since rare materials cost more. If the feedstock is too expensive, alternatives might have to be investigated. Energy derived from oil and gas fluctuates in price, but always becomes expensive in times of tension in the producing areas.
Opportunities for recycling	If unreacted starting materials can be fed back into the chemical reactor to form new products, this will improve the efficiency and profitability of the process. If water used in the process can be recycled, this reduces waste.	If it is very difficult to separate unreacted starting materials at the end of reaction, this makes the reaction inefficient and wasteful.
Energy requirements	Exothermic reactions can be used to sustain the heat in a reaction or heat the building. This saves money on energy costs. Many chemical reactions use catalysts to speed up the rate of reaction rather than using higher temperatures. This can allow more control of the reaction products and saves energy.	Reactions which require heating can be very costly as energy (gas, electricity) must be purchased. Reactions which require cooling can also be expensive as energy must be removed from the reaction by surrounding with a coolant.
Use of by-products	Many reactions produce more than one product. If the other product(s) can be used elsewhere in the process, this will save money. If the by-products can be sold to other companies, this will also increase profit.	If the by-products are toxic, very corrosive or environmentally damaging, it will be expensive to deal with these. For example, acidic gases like sulfur dioxide (SO_2) and the greenhouse gas carbon dioxide (CO_2) can be costly for companies to deal with.
Yield of product	A high yield of product is very profitable.	Low yields cost money as time and energy must be put in to run the reaction several times to produce enough of the desired product.

Key points !

∗ Industrial processes are designed to maximise profit and minimise the impact on the environment.

∗ Factors that influence the design of a chemical process include: availability, sustainability and cost of feedstocks; opportunities for recycling; energy requirements; use of by-products; product yield.

∗ Environmental considerations include: minimising waste; avoiding the use or production of toxic substances; designing products which will biodegrade.

Hints & tips

It is common for scientists and engineers to represent chemical reactions using flow diagrams. An example is shown in Figure 11.1, which shows how ethanol is made by reacting ethene with water.

You should be able to look at these diagrams and apply your chemical knowledge.

1 Look out for opportunities to **recycle**. In this case, unreacted ethene from separator A could be fed back into the reaction vessel.

2 Look out for evidence of **endo- or exothermic reactions**. In this case, a cooler is used suggesting that the reaction between ethene and water is exothermic. This has a cost consideration as cooling (and heating) can be expensive.

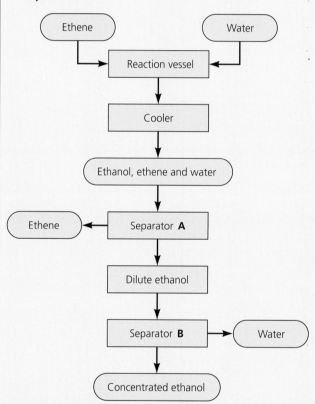

Figure 11.1 Representing a chemical reaction using a flow diagram

3 Think about how chemicals can be **separated**. Solids can be removed from liquids using **filtration**, and **distillation** can be used for separating a mixture of liquids. In this case, it is likely that distillation is the process used in separator B to separate water and ethanol.

4 Look for **environmentally damaging** products or **by-products**. In this case, water is produced from separator B. It would make sense to feed this water back into the reaction vessel.

Study questions

1 Hydrogen gas can be made on an industrial scale using the sulfur–iodine cycle. There are three steps in the sulfur–iodine cycle:

Step 1: $I_2 + SO_2 + 2H_2O \rightarrow 2HI + H_2SO_4$

Step 2: $2HI \rightarrow I_2 + H_2$

Step 3: $H_2SO_4 \rightarrow SO_2 + H_2O + \frac{1}{2}O_2$

   a) Suggest why care must be taken to ensure the products of step 3 are not released into the atmosphere.

   b) Why does step 3 help to reduce the cost of manufacturing hydrogen?

   c) Write the overall equation for the sulfur–iodine cycle.

2 Urea, $(NH_2)_2CO$, is an important industrial chemical that is mainly used in fertilisers. It is made by the Bosch–Meiser process.

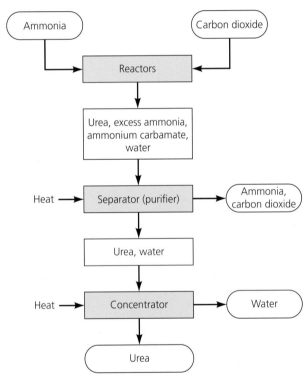

   Figure 11.2

   a) In the reactors, the production of urea involves two reversible reactions.
   In the first reaction ammonium carbamate is produced.

   $2NH_3(g) + CO_2(g) \rightleftharpoons H_2NCOONH_4(g)$

   In the second reaction the ammonium carbamate decomposes to form urea.

   $H_2NCOONH_4(g) \rightleftharpoons (NH_2)_2CO(g) + H_2O(g)$

   A chemical plant produces 530 tonnes of urea per day. Calculate the theoretical mass, in tonnes, of ammonia required to produce 530 tonnes of urea.

   b) Add a line to a copy of the flow chart to show how the Bosch–Meiser process can be made more economical.

Chapter 12
Calculations from equations

Making a new product requires chemists to work with chemical equations to allow them to calculate how much product they are likely to make or how much reactant they will require. For Higher Chemistry you should be comfortable working with equations involving masses, volumes, concentrations and moles.

Calculations involving mass

Example

Calculate the mass of water produced when 320 g of methane is burned according to the following equation:

$$CH_4 + 2O_2 \rightarrow CO_2 + 2H_2O$$

When faced with a question like this, it can help to work through it using the following five steps:

Step 1: Write a balanced chemical equation (unless already given).

Step 2: Identify the two chemicals referred to in the question and write the mole ratio.

Step 3: Calculate the moles of the substance you have been given a mass for (in this instance, methane). Note that gfm stands for gram formula mass.

Step 4: Use the mole ratio to calculate the number of moles of the other substance (in this case, water).

Step 5: Calculate the mass.

Solution

Step 1: $CH_4 + 2O_2 \rightarrow CO_2 + 2H_2O$

Step 2: 1 mole $CH_4 \rightarrow$ 2 moles H_2O

Step 3: $Mole = \frac{mass}{gfm} = \frac{320}{16} = 20$ moles

Step 4: From our mole ratio in Step 2, we know that 20 moles $CH_4 \rightarrow$ 40 moles H_2O.

Step 5: Mass = moles × gfm

$= 40 \times 18$

$= 720$ g

Therefore, 720 g of water is produced when 320 g of methane is burned.

Calculations involving volumes and concentrations of solutions

Example

Calculate the concentration of hydrochloric acid used if 20 cm³ of the acid was neutralised by 10 cm³ of 1 mol l⁻¹ sodium hydroxide solution.

In a question involving volumes and concentrations, it can help to work through six useful steps.

Step 1: Write a balanced chemical equation (unless already given).

Step 2: Identify the two chemicals referred to in the question and write the mole ratio.

Step 3: Write down the volumes, in litres, and the concentrations under the reactants.

Step 4: Calculate the number of moles of the chemical with the most information. Use moles = concentration × volume.

Step 5: Use the mole ratio to work out the moles of the other reactant (in this case, 1 mole of acid reacts with 1 mole of alkali).

Step 6: Calculate the volume, concentration or mass of the chemical you are asked to find out.

Solution

Step 1: $HCl + NaOH \rightarrow H_2O + NaCl$

Step 2: 1 mole of HCl reacts with 1 mole of NaOH

Step 3: Volume of HCl = 20 cm³ = 0.02 l; concentration = ?

Volume of NaOH = 10 cm³ = 0.01 l; concentration = 1 mol l⁻¹

Step 4: Moles of NaOH = concentration × volume = CV = 1 × 0.01 = 0.01

Step 5: Since 1 mole of alkali reacts with 1 mole of acid, moles HCl = 0.01

Step 6: Concentration of HCl = $\frac{moles}{volume}$

$$= \frac{0.01}{0.02}$$

$$= 0.5 \text{ mol l}^{-1}$$

Therefore, hydrochloric acid of concentration 0.5 mol l⁻¹ is used.

Calculations involving masses, volumes and concentrations of solutions

Example

Calculate the mass of calcium carbonate required to react completely with 300 cm³ of 0.1 mol l⁻¹ hydrochloric acid.

⇨
Solution

$$CaCO_3 + 2HCl \rightarrow CaCl_2 + CO_2 + H_2O$$

1 mole   2 moles

$$\text{Moles of acid} = CV = 0.1 \times 0.3 = 0.03$$

$$\text{Moles of } CaCO_3 = \frac{0.03}{2}$$

So number of moles of $CaCO_3 = 0.015$ moles

Mass $CaCO_3 = 0.015 \times 100$

Therefore, 1.5 g of calcium carbonate is needed to react completely with the acid.

Calculations involving excess reactant

The previous examples have only considered the effect of one reactant on the quantity of product obtained. In reality, you would have to consider the quantities of all the reactants and then determine how they would affect the product. This can be done by deciding which reactant is in excess. The reactant in excess will not control how much product is obtained since some of this reactant will remain unreacted (there is too much of it). For these calculations, you should focus your attention on the reactant which is not in excess since this will control how much product is obtained.

Example

15 g of calcium carbonate were reacted with 50 cm³ of 4 mol l⁻¹ hydrochloric acid.

a) Show by calculation which reactant was present in excess.
b) Calculate the mass of carbon dioxide produced.

Solution

$$CaCO_3 + 2HCl \rightarrow CaCl_2 + CO_2 + H_2O$$
1 mol   2 mol   1 mol

a) Number of moles of $CaCO_3 = \frac{mass}{gfm}$

$$= \frac{15}{100}$$

$$= 0.15 \text{ mol}$$

Number of moles of $HCl = C \times V$

$$= 4 \times \frac{50}{1000}$$

$$= 0.2 \text{ mol}$$

According to the equation, 1 mol of $CaCO_3$ neutralises 2 mol of HCl.

Hence, 0.1 mol of $CaCO_3$ neutralises 0.2 mol of HCl.

Since there is more than 0.1 mol of $CaCO_3$ present, this reactant is in excess.

b) To calculate the mass of carbon dioxide produced we use the quantity of the reactant which is completely reacted, in other words the acid, and not the one which is present in excess.

⇨

⇨ According to the equation, 2 mol of HCl produce 1 mol of CO_2.
Hence, 0.2 mol of HCl produce 0.1 mol of CO_2.

Mass of CO_2 = moles × gfm

$$= 0.1 × 44$$
$$= 4.4 \text{ g}$$

Therefore, 4.4 g of carbon dioxide is produced in this reaction.

Example

1.2 g of magnesium was added to 80 cm³ of 2 mol l⁻¹ hydrochloric acid.

Mg + 2HCl → MgCl₂ + H₂

a) **Show by calculation which reactant was in excess.**
b) **Calculate the mass of hydrogen produced.**

Solution

a) Number of moles of Mg = $\frac{1.2}{24.3}$ = 0.05 moles

Number of moles of HCl = 2 × 0.08 = 0.16
From the equation, 1 mole of Mg reacts with 2 moles of HCl.
In other words, 0.05 mol Mg will react with 0.1 mol HCl.
Therefore, the HCl is in excess.

b) 1 mol Mg produces 1 mol H₂ so 0.05 mol Mg → 0.05 mol H₂

Mass of H₂ = 0.05 × 2 = 0.1 g

Therefore, 0.1 g of hydrogen is produced in this reaction.

Calculations involving gases

In order to tackle calculations involving gases, we must consider the **molar volume**. This concept states that the volume of 1 mole of any gas is the same, provided the temperature and pressure are constant. The relationship between molar volume, volume and number of moles is shown in Figure 12.1.

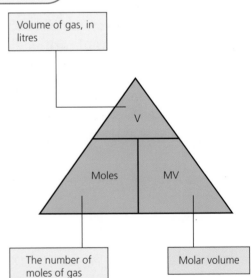

Volume of gas, in litres

V

Moles

MV

The number of moles of gas

Molar volume

Figure 12.1 This triangle will help with calculations involving molar volume.

Example

The molar volume at 0 °C and 1 atmosphere pressure is 22.4 litres mol⁻¹. Calculate

a) **the volume of 0.025 mol of oxygen**
b) **the number of moles of nitrogen in 4.48 litres under these conditions.**

⇨

⇨

Solution

a) The volume of gas = moles × MV

$$= 0.025 \times 22.4$$
$$= 0.56 \text{ litres}$$

b) The number of moles of nitrogen $= \dfrac{V}{MV}$

$$= \dfrac{4.48}{22.4}$$
$$= 0.2 \text{ moles}$$

Example

Assuming the molar volume is 24 litres mol⁻¹, calculate:

a) the volume of 3 mol of $SO_2(g)$
b) the number of moles of He in 200 cm³ He gas.

Solution

a) Volume of $SO_2 = 3 \times 24$

$$= 72 \text{ litres}$$

b) Number of moles $= \dfrac{0.2}{24}$

$$= 0.0083$$

Example

Calculate the volume of carbon dioxide released when 0.4 g of calcium carbonate is dissolved in excess hydrochloric acid. The gas is collected at room temperature and pressure. The molar volume is 24 litres mol⁻¹. The equation for the reaction is

$$CaCO_3(s) + 2HCl(aq) \rightarrow CaCl_2(aq) + CO_2(g) + H_2O(l)$$

Solution

This calculation is treated in exactly the same way as previous calculations from equations except that we must consider the volume of gas rather than the mass.

1 mole of calcium carbonate → 1 mole of carbon dioxide gas

Number of moles of $CaCO_3 = \dfrac{0.4}{100}$

$$= 0.004 \rightarrow 0.004 \text{ moles of } CO_2$$

1 mole of CO_2 → 24 litres

0.004 moles → 0.004 × 24 = 0.096 litres

Therefore, 0.096 litres of carbon dioxide is released.

Comparing volumes of gases

Using the fact that the volume of 1 mole of a gas will be the same for all gases, at specific temperatures and pressures, we can carry out quick calculations for reactions where the reactants and products are gases.

For example, nitrogen dioxide gas can be produced by reacting nitrogen with oxygen according to the equation:

$$N_2(g) + 2O_2(g) \rightarrow 2NO_2(g)$$

This balanced equation tells us that 1 mol of nitrogen reacts with 2 mol of oxygen to produce 2 mol of nitrogen dioxide. Comparing volumes, we could say that:

- 10 litres of N_2 would require 20 litres of O_2 to react and would produce 20 litres of NO_2
- 50 cm³ of N_2 would require 100 cm³ of O_2 to react and would produce 100 cm³ of NO_2.

It is important to note that this concept is only applicable to gaseous reactants and products.

Example

Assuming that all volumes are measured at 150 °C and 1 atmosphere pressure, calculate

a) the volume of oxygen required for the complete combustion of 100 cm³ of methane
b) the volume of each product.

Solution

	$CH_4(g) + 2O_2(g) \rightarrow CO_2(g) + 2H_2O(g)$			
Mole ratio	1	2	1	2
Volume ratio	1	2	1	2
Volumes given in question	100 cm³			
Volume of oxygen required		200 cm³		
Volume of products			100 cm³	200 cm³

Hence 100 cm³ of methane

a) requires 200 cm³ of oxygen for complete combustion
b) produces 100 cm³ of $CO_2(g)$ and 200 cm³ of $H_2O(g)$.

Example

A mixture of 20 cm³ of propane and 130 cm³ of oxygen was ignited and allowed to cool. Calculate the volume and composition of the resulting gaseous mixture. All volumes are measured under the same conditions of room temperature and pressure.

Solution

	$C_3H_8(g) + 5O_2(g) \rightarrow 3CO_2(g) + 4H_2O(l)$			
Mole ratio	1	5	3	4
Volume ratio	1	5	3	4
Volumes given in question	20 cm³	130 cm³		
Volume of oxygen required from reacting 20 cm³		100 cm³		
Volume remaining	0 cm³	30 cm³	60 cm³	

$\Rightarrow$

⇨
According to the equation,

$20 \, cm^3$ of propane requires $5 \times 20 \, cm^3$ of oxygen, i.e. $100 \, cm^3$.

Hence, oxygen is present in excess since its initial volume is $130 \, cm^3$.

Volume of excess oxygen $= (130 - 100) \, cm^3 = 30 \, cm^3$

Volume of carbon dioxide formed $= (3 \times 20) \, cm^3 = 60 \, cm^3$

Therefore the resulting gas mixture consists of $30 \, cm^3$ of O_2 and $60 \, cm^3$ of CO_2.

Example

Calculate the volume of carbon dioxide produced at room temperature and pressure when 0.4 g of calcium carbonate is added to $12 \, cm^3$ of $0.5 \, mol^{-1}$ hydrochloric acid. The molar volume is $24 \, litres \, mol^{-1}$.

Solution

$CaCO_3(s) + 2HCl(aq) \rightarrow CaCl_2(aq) + CO_2(g) + H_2O(l)$

1 mol   2 mol   1 mol

100 g   24 litres

Number of moles of calcium carbonate $= \dfrac{0.4}{100}$

$= 0.004$

Number of moles of hydrochloric acid $= 0.5 \times \dfrac{12}{1000}$

$= 0.006$

According to the equation, 1 mol of $CaCO_3$ requires 2 mol of HCl.

Therefore, $0.004 \, mol \, CaCO_3$ requires $0.008 \, mol \, HCl$.

The number of moles of acid present is less than this, so the $CaCO_3$ is in excess and as a result the volume of CO_2 produced will depend on the number of moles of acid.

$2 \, mol \, of \, HCl \rightarrow 1 \, mol \, of \, CO_2$

$0.006 \, mol \, HCl \rightarrow 0.003 \, mol \, CO_2$

Hence, the volume of CO_2 produced $= 0.003 \times 24$ litres

$= 0.072$ litres (or $72 \, cm^3$).

Percentage yield

The **percentage yield** is a simple way of comparing the amount of product actually obtained from a reaction with the amount expected. For example, if you calculated that you should obtain 400 kg of a medicine from a chemical reaction but when you did the reaction you only made 100 kg, the percentage yield would be 25%.

Remember

$percentage \, yield = \dfrac{actual \, yield}{theoretical \, yield} \times 100$

Example

12 g of CO_2 was obtained by reacting 6 g of C in excess oxygen. Calculate the percentage yield.

Solution

$C + O_2 \rightarrow CO_2$

Number of moles of $C = \dfrac{6}{12} = 0.5$

0.5 moles of $C \rightarrow 0.5$ moles CO_2

Mass of $CO_2 = 0.5 \times 44 = 22$ g

In other words, the theoretical yield of CO_2 is 22 g.

Percentage yield $= \dfrac{\text{actual yield}}{\text{theoretical yield}} \times 100$

$ = \dfrac{12}{22} \times 100$

$ = 54.5\%$

Example

4.5 g of H_2O was produced when 8 g of CH_4 was reacted with excess oxygen. Calculate the percentage yield.

Solution

$CH_4 + 2O_2 \rightarrow CO_2 + 2H_2O$

Number of moles of $CH_4 = \dfrac{8}{16} = 0.5$

0.5 moles $CH_4 \rightarrow 1$ mole H_2O

Mass of $H_2O = 1 \times 18 = 18$ g

In other words, the theoretical yield of H_2O is 18 g.

Percentage yield $= \dfrac{\text{actual yield}}{\text{theoretical yield}} \times 100$

$ = \dfrac{4.5}{18} \times 100$

$ = 25\%$

Example

Calculate the actual mass of SO_2 produced from reacting 28 g of sulfur with excess oxygen, according to the equation shown, assuming the percentage yield is 48%.

$S + O_2 \rightarrow SO_2$

Solution

Number of moles of $S = \dfrac{28}{32.1} = 0.872$

Since 1 mole of $S \rightarrow 1$ mole of SO_2, the mass of $SO_2 = 0.872 \times 64.1 = 55.9$ g

48% of 55.9 g $= \dfrac{48}{100} \times 55.9 = 26.8$ g

Using the percentage yield

Percentage yield is one of the factors taken into consideration when deciding on the best route to use to make a product. A reaction with a high percentage yield is always desired but will be rejected if the cost of reactants is very expensive. If an alternative reaction can be found with cheaper reactants, this might be used even if the percentage yield is lower. A cost analysis can be done to compare the costs for producing the same quantity of product.

Atom economy

The percentage yield tells us how successful the reaction is at converting reactants into products, but it does not give us information on how many by-products are formed. A reaction which produces lots of products can be problematic and wasteful. A reaction where most of the reactant atoms end up in the product is desirable. Chemists can apply the concept of **atom economy** to examine the proportion of reactants converted into the desired product.

Remember

$$atom\ economy = \frac{mass\ of\ desired\ product(s)}{total\ mass\ of\ reactants} \times 100$$

Example

Hydrogen gas can be obtained by reacting methane gas with steam.

$$CH_4 + H_2O \rightarrow CO + 3H_2$$

Calculate the atom economy for this reaction where hydrogen is the desired product.

Solution

Mass of desired product (from the equation) $= 3 \times$ gfm H_2

$$= 3 \times 2$$
$$= 6\ g$$

Total mass of reactants $=$ gfm $CH_4 +$ gfm $H_2O = 16 + 18 = 34\ g$

Atom economy $= \frac{6}{34} \times 100 = 17.65\%$

Example

Calculate the atom economy for the production of propyl ethanoate, assuming that all reactants are converted into products, according to the following equation:

$$C_3H_7OH + CH_3COOH \rightarrow C_3H_7OOCCH_3 + H_2O$$

Solution

Mass of desired product (from the equation) $= 102\ g$

Total mass of reactants $= 120\ g$

Atom economy $= \frac{102}{120} \times 100 = 85\%$

This is a high atom economy which suggests that making the ester by this method does not create much waste. An examination of the equation shows that the other product is water which is easy to deal with as it is not toxic, flammable or highly corrosive.

Key points

* The mass or volume of a product can be calculated using appropriate data and balanced chemical equations.
* Balanced chemical equations and calculations involving mass, volume and concentration can be used to calculate reactants in excess.
* The percentage yield can be found using the expression

$$\text{Percentage yield} = \frac{\text{actual yield}}{\text{theoretical yield}} \times 100$$

* The atom economy can be calculated using the expression

$$\text{atom economy} = \frac{\text{mass of desired product(s)}}{\text{total mass of reactants}} \times 100$$

Hints & tips

This chapter has examined several calculation types you are likely to encounter in Higher Chemistry. Chemists are expected to be numerate so you can expect several of these calculations in your final exam. Practise each calculation several times and develop a technique that works for you. Make sure you can recognise the different calculation types and apply the correct method. Layout of calculations is as important as accuracy. Take your time calculating formula masses, show your working and always go back and check your answers.

Study questions

Calculation involving mass

1 Calculate the mass of carbon dioxide produced when 6 g of propane reacts completely with oxygen in the following reaction:

$$C_3H_8 + 5O_2 \rightarrow 3CO_2 + 4H_2O$$

Calculations involving mass, concentration and volume

2 Calculate the volume of $2\,mol\,l^{-1}$ hydrochloric acid required to neutralise $100\,cm^3$ of $1\,mol\,l^{-1}$ sodium hydroxide.

$$HCl + NaOH \rightarrow NaCl + H_2O$$

3 Calculate the mass of magnesium required to react completely with $150\,cm^3$ of $0.5\,mol\,l^{-1}$ hydrochloric acid.

$$Mg + 2HCl \rightarrow MgCl_2 + H_2$$

Calculations involving excess reagent

4 Calculate the mass of water produced by reacting 8 g of hydrogen with 16 g of oxygen.

$$H_2 + \frac{1}{2}O_2 \rightarrow H_2O$$

5 Calculate the mass of hydrogen sulfide produced by reacting 24 g of iron (II) sulfide with $200\,cm^3$ of $2\,mol\,l^{-1}$ hydrochloric acid.

$$FeS(s) + 2HCl(aq) \rightarrow FeCl_2(aq) + H_2S(g)$$

6 In an experiment, 2 g of calcium oxide was reacted with 50 cm^3 of 0.5 mol l^{-1} sulfuric acid.

$$CaO + H_2SO_4 \rightarrow CaSO_4 + H_2O$$

  a) Show by calculation that the calcium oxide is in excess.

  b) Calculate the mass of calcium sulfate produced.

Calculations involving gas volumes (assume molar volume = 24 litres mol^{-1})

7 Calculate the volume of hydrogen produced when 6 g of magnesium is reacted with 100 cm^3 of 1 mol l^{-1} hydrochloric acid.

$$Mg + 2HCl \rightarrow MgCl_2 + H_2$$

8 Copper carbonate decomposes to produce copper oxide and carbon dioxide. Calculate the volume of carbon dioxide produced from decomposing 40 g of copper carbonate.

$$CuCO_3 \rightarrow CuO + CO_2$$

Calculations involving gas volumes

9 State the volume and composition of remaining gases when 100 cm^3 propane is reacted with 600 cm^3 of oxygen gas.

$$C_3H_8(g) + 5O_2(g) \rightarrow 3CO_2(g) + 4H_2O(g)$$

10 Calculate the volume of hydrogen required to react completely with 4 litres of oxygen gas.

$$H_2 + \frac{1}{2}O_2 \rightarrow H_2O$$

Calculations involving percentage yield and atom economy

11 Ethyl 2-cyanoacrylate is synthesised from ethyl 2-cyanoethanoate by a process based on the Knovenagel reaction.

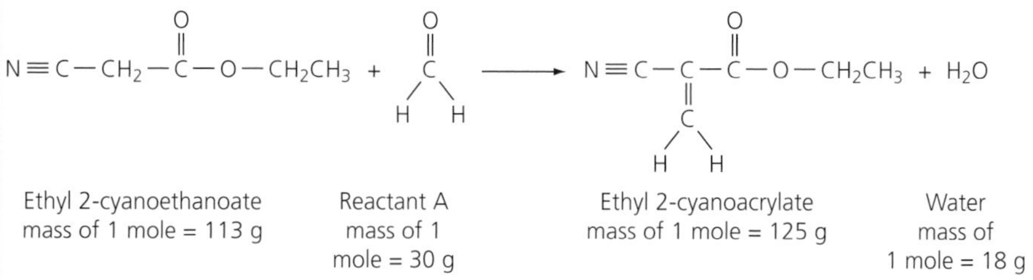

$$N\equiv C-CH_2-\overset{\overset{\displaystyle O}{\|}}{C}-O-CH_2CH_3 \ + \ \overset{\overset{\displaystyle O}{\|}}{\underset{H\quad H}{C}} \longrightarrow N\equiv C-\overset{\overset{\displaystyle O}{\|}}{\underset{\underset{H\quad H}{\overset{\displaystyle \|}{C}}}{C}}-O-CH_2CH_3 \ + \ H_2O$$

Ethyl 2-cyanoethanoate | Reactant A | Ethyl 2-cyanoacrylate | Water
mass of 1 mole = 113 g | mass of 1 mole = 30 g | mass of 1 mole = 125 g | mass of 1 mole = 18 g

Figure 12.2

  a) Name reactant A.

  b) Name this type of chemical reaction.

  c) Calculate the atom economy for the formation of ethyl 2-cyanoacrylate using this process. Show your working clearly.

  d) In an experiment, 2 kg of ethyl 2-cyanoethanoate was reacted with an excess of reactant A to produce 1.5 kg of ethyl 2-cyanoacrylate. Calculate the percentage yield.

12 Ammonia is manufactured from hydrogen and nitrogen by the **Haber process**. If 80 kg of ammonia is produced from 60 kg of hydrogen, what is the percentage yield?

$N_2 + 3H_2 \rightleftharpoons 2NH_3$

A $\dfrac{80}{340} \times 100$

B $\dfrac{80}{170} \times 100$

C $\dfrac{30}{80} \times 100$

D $\dfrac{60}{80} \times 100$

13 Methanamide, $HCONH_2$, is widely used in industry to make nitrogen compounds. It is also used as a solvent as it can dissolve ionic compounds.

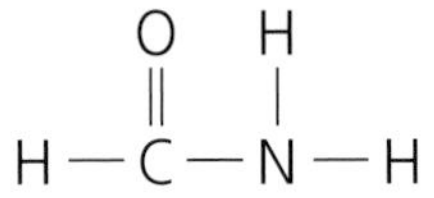

$$\begin{array}{ccc} O & & H \\ \| & & | \\ H-C&-N&-H \end{array}$$

Figure 12.3

a) Why is methanamide a suitable solvent for ionic compounds?

b) In industry, methanamide is produced by the reaction of an ester with ammonia.

$HCOOCH_3$	+	NH_3	$\rightarrow$	$HCONH_2$	+	CH_3OH
mass of		mass of		mass of		mass of
1 mole = 60.0 g		1 mole = 17.0 g		1 mole = 45.0 g		1 mole = 32.0 g

   i. Name the ester used in the industrial production of methanamide.

   ii. Calculate the atom economy for the production of methanamide.

   iii. 12 kg of ester was reacted with excess ammonia. Assuming an 82% yield, calculate the mass of methanamide actually produced.

Chapter 13
Equilibria

The concept of **equilibrium** is applied to **reversible reactions**. We say that a chemical reaction is in a state of equilibrium when the rate of the forward reaction is equal to the rate of the reverse reaction. Chemists try to influence chemical reactions by favouring the forward reaction – in other words, the making of the product – as this will maximise profit. This can be done by changing the concentration of reactants or products, changing the pressure and changing the temperature. If a reaction at equilibrium is subjected to a change in one of these factors, the equilibrium position will adjust to counteract this change, for example if a reaction at equilibrium is cooled, the reaction will shift to counteract this change, i.e. the reaction which produces heat will be favoured.

Changing the concentration

Consider the reaction

$$A + B \rightleftharpoons C + D$$

If the concentration of A or B is increased, the original equilibrium will be upset. As a result, more C and D will be produced until a new equilibrium is established. This is known as the equilibrium *shifting to the right*.

Likewise, if C or D was removed as it was produced, the equilibrium would again shift to the right, making more C and D.

This is illustrated by considering the equilibrium that exists in a bottle of bromine water:

$$Br_2(l) + H_2O(l) \rightleftharpoons Br^-(aq) + BrO^-(aq) + 2H^+(aq)$$

When the equilibrium shifts, there is a detectable colour change as the bromine liquid has a brown colour and the product ions are colourless.

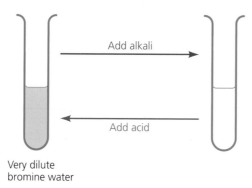

Very dilute
bromine water

Figure 13.1 Changing the position of equilibrium by altering the concentration of reactants or products

Adding $OH^-(aq)$, from an alkali such as $NaOH(aq)$, removes H^+ ions to form water. This causes the equilibrium to shift to the right which results in the solution becoming colourless. If an acid is added (a source of H^+ ions) the equilibrium will shift to the left to counteract the change. This causes the solution to adopt a brown colour.

> ## Example
>
> Iodine monochloride (a brown liquid) can react with chlorine gas to form the yellow solid iodine trichloride:
>
> $$ICl(l) + Cl_2(g) \rightleftharpoons ICl_3(s)$$
>
> State what would be observed if the following changes were made to this reaction at equilibrium:
>
> **a)** excess chlorine was added
> **b)** chlorine gas was removed from the reaction.
>
> ### Solution
>
> **a)** Adding more chlorine would cause the equilibrium to shift to the right, producing more yellow $ICl_3(s)$.
> **b)** Removing the chlorine would cause the equilibrium to shift to the left, causing the yellow solid to be converted into chlorine gas and brown liquid ICl.

Changing the temperature

In a reversible reaction, if the forward reaction is exothermic, the reverse reaction must be endothermic. If a reaction at equilibrium is exposed to a rise in temperature, the equilibrium will shift to favour the side which absorbs heat. In other words, the reaction will shift to the endothermic side. A fall in temperature will cause the reaction to favour the exothermic process. This is illustrated by observing the equilibrium that exists between dinitrogen tetroxide (a colourless gas) and nitrogen dioxide (a brown gas):

$$N_2O_4(g) \rightleftharpoons 2NO_2(g) \quad \Delta H = +ve$$
colourless   brown

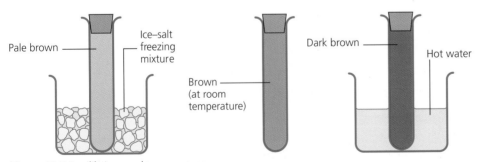

Figure 13.2 Equilibrium and temperature

Increasing the temperature causes the equilibrium to shift to the right (the endothermic reaction) which results in the gas mixture darkening in colour.

Lowering the temperature causes the equilibrium to shift to the left (the exothermic reaction) which results in the gas mixture lightening in colour.

Example

Steam reforming of coal can be used to produce a valuable mixture of carbon monoxide and hydrogen. The forward reaction is endothermic. State how a change in temperature on this reaction at equilibrium could affect the yield of CO and H_2.

$$C + H_2O \rightleftharpoons CO + H_2 \qquad \Delta H = +131\,kJ\,mol^{-1}$$

Solution

Increasing the temperature will increase the yield of CO and H_2 since the forward reaction is endothermic.

Hints & tips

When thinking about the effect of temperature on equilibrium it can be useful to imagine a house with a central heating system and an air conditioning system controlled by a thermostat. The thermostat detects when the temperature changes and will adjust conditions in the house so that the temperature gets back to the desired level. If the temperature falls, for example in the winter, a signal is sent to the boiler to increase the central heating output so that the house is heated. If the temperature rises beyond a comfortable level, such as in the summer, a signal is sent to turn on the air conditioning to cool the air back to the desired temperature. You can think of the boiler as the exothermic process and the air conditioning as the endothermic process.

A rise in temperature will favour the endothermic process. A fall in temperature will favour the exothermic process.

Changing the pressure

Changing the pressure of gases at equilibrium causes a shift to readjust the pressure. In other words, if the pressure is increased, the equilibrium will shift to the side which causes the pressure to decrease. If the pressure is decreased, the equilibrium will shift to the side which causes an increase in pressure. In chemical reactions, the side of the equation with the most gaseous atoms or molecules will have the highest pressure.

For example:

$$2SO_2(g) + O_2(g) \rightleftharpoons 2SO_3(g)$$

In this equation, the left-hand side has 3 moles of gas while the right-hand side has 2 moles of gas. Increasing the pressure will cause the equilibrium to shift to the right.

Consider the N_2O_4–NO_2 system which we met earlier in this chapter:

$$N_2O_4(g) \rightleftharpoons 2NO_2(g)$$
colourless   brown

Increasing the pressure will cause a shift to the left. Decreasing the pressure will cause a shift to the right.

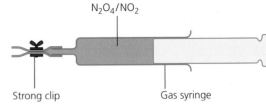

N_2O_4/NO_2

Strong clip   Gas syringe

Figure 13.3 Pushing in the plunger of this gas syringe causes the pressure to increase. A lightening of colour is observed as the equilibrium shifts to the left to produce more colourless N_2O_4 molecules.

Hints & tips

When considering the effect of pressure it is important to remember that only reactants and products in the gaseous state should be considered. Solids, liquids and solutions should be ignored. We can use the reaction between chlorine and water as an example.

$$Cl_2(g) + H_2O(l) \rightleftharpoons Cl^-(aq) + ClO^-(aq) + 2H^+(aq)$$

In this equilibrium, there is 1 mole of gas on the left-hand side and 0 moles on the right-hand side. Increasing the pressure would cause a shift to the right. Where there is an equal number of moles of gas on both sides, pressure will have no effect on the equilibrium position. For example:

$$CO(g) + H_2O(g) \rightleftharpoons CO_2(g) + H_2(g)$$

The effect of a catalyst

Catalysts have no effect on the position of equilibrium. As can be seen from Figure 13.4, catalysts work by lowering the activation energy. Since they lower the activation energy of both the forward and reverse reaction by the same amount, they do not affect the position of equilibrium. They do, however, allow the reaction to reach equilibrium more quickly.

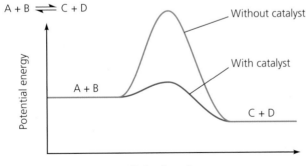

$A + B \rightleftharpoons C + D$

Potential energy

Without catalyst

With catalyst

A + B

C + D

Path of reaction

Figure 13.4 Potential energy diagram for a catalysed and uncatalysed reaction

Key points

* A reversible reaction is said to have attained a state of dynamic equilibrium when the rate of the forward reaction is equal to the rate of the reverse reaction.
* Concentration of reactants or products, temperature and pressure can all affect a system at equilibrium. The system will adjust to counteract the change.
* A catalyst does not affect the position of equilibrium.

Summary

Change applied	Effect on equilibrium position
Concentration Addition of reactant or removal of product Addition of product or removal of reactant	 Equilibrium shifts to the right Equilibrium shifts to the left
Temperature Increase Decrease	 Shifts in direction of endothermic reaction Shifts in direction of exothermic reaction
Pressure Increase Decrease	 Shifts in direction which reduces the number of molecules in gas phase Shifts in direction which increases the number of molecules in gas phase
Catalyst	No effect on equilibrium position; equilibrium more rapidly attained

Study questions

1 Which of the following statements about the use of a catalyst in a reaction at equilibrium is false?
   A The rate of the reverse reaction will be increased.
   B The time taken to reach equilibrium will decrease.
   C The position of equilibrium will shift to the right.
   D The activation energy of the reaction will decrease.

2 In which of the following reactions will an increase in pressure have no effect on the position of equilibrium?
   A $2SO_2(g) + O_2(g) \rightleftharpoons 2SO_3(g)$
   B $N_2(g) + 2O_2(g) \rightleftharpoons 2NO_2(g)$
   C $H_2(g) + Cl_2(g) \rightleftharpoons 2HCl(g)$
   D $N_2 + 3H_2 \rightleftharpoons 2NH_3(g)$

3 The chromate/dichromate equilibrium is useful for studying factors that can affect equilibrium since the ions have a different colour.
   $2CrO_4^{2-}(aq) + 2H^+(aq) \rightleftharpoons Cr_2O_7^{2-}(aq) + H_2O(l)$
      (yellow)   (orange)

   a) Explain why adding KOH(aq) causes the solution to become more yellow in colour.
   b) State the effect of adding sulfuric acid to the solution.

4   The industrial process used to manufacture ammonia is known as the Haber process. This involves reacting nitrogen with hydrogen to form ammonia:

$$N_2 + 3H_2 \rightleftharpoons 2NH_3(g) \quad \Delta H = -92\,kJ$$

a) With reference to this equation, explain the effect of increasing the temperature on the
   i.   speed of reaction
   ii. yield of ammonia.
b) With reference to this equation, explain the effect of increasing the pressure.
c) In the Haber process, the ammonia formed is continuously removed. State how this affects the position of equilibrium.

5   Phosphorus pentachloride decomposes according to the following equation:

$$PCl_5(g) \rightleftharpoons PCl_3(g) + Cl_2(g) \quad \Delta H = +124\,kJ$$

State the effect on the concentration of PCl_3 if
a) the concentration of chlorine is increased
b) the PCl_3 formed is continuously removed
c) the temperature is decreased
d) the pressure is increased.

Chapter 14

Chemical energy

Enthalpy

The change in energy in a chemical reaction is known as the *enthalpy change*. In the exothermic reaction illustrated by the energy profile diagram in Figure 14.1, the energy of the products is 20 kJ and the energy of the reactants is 60 kJ. The enthalpy change for this reaction is the difference between products and reactants, in other words $(20 - 60)kJ = -40 kJ$. This tells us that the reaction is exothermic as 40 kJ has been 'lost' to the surroundings.

Chemists are interested in enthalpy changes, especially for industrial processes, since they can have health, safety and cost considerations. For example, a highly exothermic reaction could require specialist reaction vessels with cooling pipes to contain the reaction. On the other hand, a highly endothermic reaction may require expensive insulation and heating at a later stage, which can be very costly.

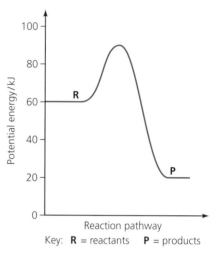

Figure 14.1 The enthalpy change in a chemical reaction is the difference between the energy of the products and reactants.

Enthalpy of combustion

The **enthalpy of combustion** is defined as the enthalpy change when one mole of a substance is burned completely in oxygen. In the lab, the enthalpy of combustion of a fuel can be measured using a set up such as the one shown in Figure 14.2.

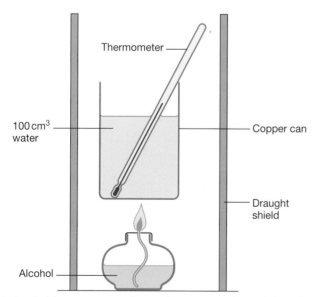

Figure 14.2 This simple lab apparatus can be used to measure the enthalpy of combustion of a fuel.

Example

4.18 kJ of energy was released when 0.20 g of methanol (CH₃OH) was burned. Calculate the enthalpy of combustion.

Solution

To find the enthalpy of combustion you have to relate the energy released to the mass of 1 mole of methanol, 32 g.

$0.20\,g \rightarrow 4.18\,kJ$

$1.00\,g \rightarrow 20.9\,kJ$

$32.00\,g \rightarrow 668.8\,kJ$

So, the enthalpy of combustion for methanol would be $-668.8\,kJ\,mol^{-1}$.

Hints & tips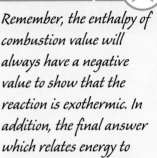

Remember, the enthalpy of combustion value will always have a negative value to show that the reaction is exothermic. In addition, the final answer which relates energy to 1 mole will have the units $kJ\,mol^{-1}$.

In the example, the energy released by burning methanol was given. To calculate the energy released from the fuel, the following equation is used:

Remember

$$E_h = cm\Delta T$$

where

c is the specific heat capacity of water, $4.18\,kJ\,kg^{-1}\,°C^{-1}$

m is the mass of water heated, in kg

ΔT is the change in temperature of the water.

Example

An experiment was carried out to calculate the enthalpy of combustion of ethanol. The results from the experiment are shown. Calculate the enthalpy of combustion of ethanol using this data.

Mass of ethanol burner at the start of the experiment = 40 g

Mass of ethanol burner at the end of the experiment = 39.8 g

Temperature of water at the start of the experiment = 22 °C

Temperature of water at the end of the experiment = 34 °C

Volume of water heated = 100 cm³

Solution

$E_h = cm\Delta T = 4.18 \times 0.1 \times 12 = 5.02\,kJ$ (to two decimal places)

Mass of ethanol burned = 0.2 g

$0.2\,g \rightarrow 5.02\,kJ$

$1.0\,g \rightarrow 25.1\,kJ$

$46\,g \rightarrow 1154.6\,kJ$

The enthalpy of combustion of ethanol is $-1155\,kJ\,mol^{-1}$.

Hints & tips

*When using information like this, it is assumed that 1 cm³ of water weighs 1 g. Since the c value of 4.18 is the amount of energy required to raise the temperature of **1 kg** of water by 1°C, you should convert this mass of water into kg, i.e. 1 cm³ = 0.01 kg.*

Experimental concerns

When using a simple calorimeter such as the one shown in Figure 14.2, the values obtained for the enthalpy of combustion are usually much lower than the theoretical values. When carrying out these experiments, not all of the fuel combusts completely and there is always some heat lost to the surroundings. Any technique which addresses these experimental concerns will give improved enthalpy values.

Hess's law

In simple terms, **Hess's law** states the following:

Remember

The enthalpy change of a chemical reaction is independent of the route taken.

This allows chemists to calculate the enthalpy changes for reactions which are often difficult to carry out. When using Hess's law, it is usual to be presented with a direct route and several alternative routes. In most cases, the enthalpy change for the direct route is equal to the sum of the enthalpy changes for all other routes. This is illustrated by the examples which follow on the next page.

The first example illustrates how Hess's law can be used to calculate the enthalpy change when carbon is reacted with hydrogen to form methane, according to the equation:

$$C(s) + 2H_2(g) \rightarrow CH_4(g)$$

In this case, the direct route is the reaction of carbon with hydrogen to form methane. An alternative route must start with the same reactants (i.e. carbon and hydrogen), end with the same products (i.e. methane) and give us enthalpy information. Enthalpies of combustion can be used for carbon, hydrogen and methane since enthalpy data for combustion is easy to obtain.

Example

$$C(s) + 2H_2(g) \rightarrow CH_4(g)$$

Calculate the enthalpy change of the above reaction using the enthalpies of combustion of carbon, hydrogen and methane.

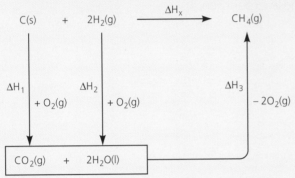

Figure 14.3

Solution

Step 1: Write equations for the enthalpy of combustion of C, H_2 and CH_4.

1 $C(s) + O_2(g) \rightarrow CO_2(g)$ $\quad\quad$ $\Delta H = -394\,kJ\,mol^{-1}$

2 $H_2(g) + \frac{1}{2}O_2(g) \rightarrow H_2O(g)$ $\quad$ $\Delta H = -286\,kJ\,mol^{-1}$

3 $CH_4(g) + 2O_2(g) \rightarrow CO_2(g) + 2H_2O(g)$ $\quad$ $\Delta H = -891\,kJ\,mol^{-1}$

The target equation is $C(s) + 2H_2(g) \rightarrow CH_4(g)$.

You have to use the ΔH combustion equations and rearrange them to resemble the target equation.

Step 2:

- Multiply equation 2) × 2 to give 2 moles of H_2.
- Reverse equation 3) so that CH_4 is a product. (If you reverse the equation, you must reverse the ΔH.)
- Rewrite all three equations and add to give the target.

1 $C(s) + O_2(g) \rightarrow CO_2(g)$ $\quad\quad$ $\Delta H = -394\,kJ\,mol^{-1}$

2 $2H_2(g) + O_2(g) \rightarrow 2H_2O(g)$ $\quad\quad$ $\Delta H = 2 \times -286\,kJ\,mol^{-1}$

3 $CO_2(g) + 2H_2O(g) \rightarrow CH_4(g) + 2O_2(g)$ $\quad$ $\Delta H = +891\,kJ\,mol^{-1}$

$\quad C(s) + 2H_2(g) \rightarrow CH_4(g)$ $\quad\quad$ $\Delta H = -394 + -572 + 891$

$\quad\quad\quad\quad\quad\quad\quad\quad\quad\quad\quad\quad\quad\quad\quad\quad$ $= -75\,kJ\,mol^{-1}$

Example

The following equation shows the formation of ethanol from carbon, hydrogen and oxygen.

$$2C(s) + 3H_2(g) + \frac{1}{2}O_2(g) \rightarrow C_2H_5OH(l)$$

Use the enthalpies of combustion of carbon, hydrogen and ethanol to calculate the enthalpy change of this reaction.

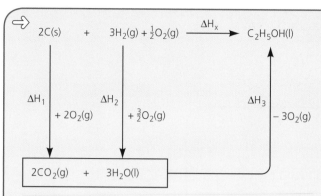

Figure 14.4

Solution

Step 1: Write equations for the enthalpy of combustion of C, H_2 and C_2H_5OH.

1 $C(s) + O_2(g) \rightarrow CO_2(g)$ $\quad\quad\quad\quad$ $\Delta H = -394\,kJ\,mol^{-1}$

2 $H_2(g) + \frac{1}{2}O_2(g) \rightarrow H_2O(g)$ $\quad\quad$ $\Delta H = -286\,kJ\,mol^{-1}$

3 $C_2H_5OH(l) + 3O_2(g) \rightarrow 2CO_2(g) + 3H_2O(l)$ $\;$ $\Delta H = -1367\,kJ\,mol^{-1}$

The target equation is $2C(s) + 3H_2(g) \rightarrow \frac{1}{2}O_2(g) \rightarrow C_2H_5OH(l)$.

You have to rearrange the ΔH combustion equations to resemble this target equation.

Step 2:

- Multiply equation 1) × 2 to give 2 moles of C.
- Multiply equation 2) × 3 to give 3 moles of H_2.
- Reverse equation 3) so that C_2H_5OH is a product.
- Rewrite all three equations and add to give the target.

1 $2C(s) + 2O_2(g) \rightarrow 2CO_2(g)$ $\quad\quad\quad\quad\quad$ $\Delta H = 2 \times -394\,kJ\,mol^{-1}$

2 $3H_2(g) + 1\frac{1}{2}O_2(g) \rightarrow 3H_2O(g)$ $\quad\quad\quad$ $\Delta H = 3 \times -286\,kJ\,mol^{-1}$

3 $2CO_2(g) + 3H_2O(l) \rightarrow C_2H_5OH(l) + 3O_2(g)$ $\quad$ $\Delta H = +1367\,kJ\,mol^{-1}$

$2C(s) + 3H_2(g) + \frac{1}{2}O_2(g) \rightarrow C_2H_5OH(l)$ $\quad\quad$ $\Delta H = -279\,kJ\,mol^{-1}$

Note: Oxygen is one of the elements present in ethanol but it is not involved in deriving the required enthalpy change. The calculation is based on enthalpies of combustion. Oxygen gas supports combustion; it does not have an enthalpy of combustion.

A quick method for solving Hess's law calculations

Example

$C(s) + 2H_2(g) \rightarrow CH_4(g)$

Calculate the enthalpy change for the above reaction using the enthalpies of combustion of carbon, hydrogen and methane.

Solution

Quick method

$\Delta H = 1 \times \Delta H_c + 2 \times \Delta H_{H_2} + (-\Delta H_{CH_4})$

$\quad = -394 + 2 \times (-286) + 891$

$\quad = -75 \text{ kJ mol}^{-1}$

Example

$2C(s) + 3H_2(g) + \frac{1}{2}O_2(g) \rightarrow C_2H_5OH(l)$

Use the enthalpies of combustion of carbon, hydrogen and ethanol to calculate the enthalpy change for this reaction.

Solution

Quick method

$\Delta H = 2 \times \Delta H_c + 3 \times \Delta H_{H_2} + (-\Delta H_{C_2H_5OH})$

$\quad = 2 \times (-394) + 3 \times (-286) + 1367$

$\quad = -279 \text{ kJ mol}^{-1}$

Hints & tips

In solving problems such as these, it is worth remembering the simple definition of Hess's law. Consider Figure 14.5, which illustrates the different routes which can be used to form water from hydrogen.

If you were asked to calculate an enthalpy change for reaction X, you would have to apply Hess's law. In such diagrams, always try to identify the direct route first. You can do this by looking for a start (where more than one arrow comes from) and an end (where more than one arrow points). Figure 14.5 tells us that $H_2(g)$ is the start and H_2O (l) is the end. In other words, the direct route is -286 kJ mol^{-1}. The sum of the enthalpy changes for all other routes must equal this value; therefore $-286 = -188 + X$. The value for X must be -98.

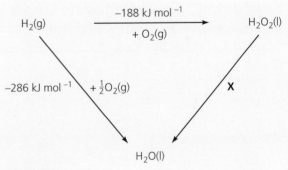

Figure 14.5

Example

Potassium chloride can be formed by the reaction of hydrochloric acid with solid potassium hydroxide (ΔH_1). An alternative route involves dissolving potassium hydroxide in water (ΔH_2) and then reacting the solution with hydrochloric acid (ΔH_3).

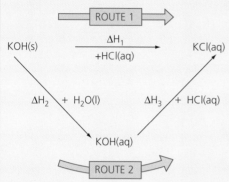

Figure 14.6 Making KCl(aq) via two routes

a) Use Hess's law to write a statement which links the three enthalpy changes shown.

b) Calculate ΔH_2 given that $\Delta H_1 = -56\,\text{kJ}\,\text{mol}^{-1}$ and $\Delta H_3 = -37\,\text{kJ}\,\text{mol}^{-1}$.

Solution

a) $\Delta H_1 = \Delta H_2 + \Delta H_3$

b) $\Delta H_2 = -19\,\text{kJ}\,\text{mol}^{-1}$

Example

Some questions involving Hess's law present you with a 'target' equation and several other equations and ask you to form a relationship between them. This is illustrated in the following question, which is a past SQA exam question from 2009.

$$S(s) + H_2(g) \rightarrow H_2S(g) \qquad \Delta H = a$$

$$H_2(g) + \tfrac{1}{2}O_2(g) \rightarrow H_2O(l) \qquad \Delta H = b$$

$$S(s) + O_2 \rightarrow SO_2(g) \qquad \Delta H = c$$

$$H_2S(g) + 1\tfrac{1}{2}O_2(g) \rightarrow H_2O\,(l) + SO_2(g) \qquad \Delta H = d$$

What is the relationship between a, b, c and d?

1 $a = b + c - d$

2 $a = d - b - c$

3 $a = b - c - d$

4 $a = d + c - b$

Solution

The answers given tell you that the first equation **1** is the target; you are looking for equations which have S(s) and $H_2(g)$ as reactants and $H_2S(g)$ as a product. Applying this, you would require equation **3** for S(s), equation **2** for $H_2(g)$ and equation **4** for $H_2S(g)$. Equation **4** must, however, be reversed so that H_2S is a product. Reversing the equation reverses the ΔH sign. Overall, $a = c + b - d$ which is answer **1**.

Bond enthalpies

The data booklet lists *bond enthalpy* data for common molecules. This data can be used to calculate the enthalpy change for chemical reactions. When carrying out such calculations, it is worth remembering that *breaking bonds requires energy* while *making bonds releases energy*.

Example

Calculate the enthalpy change, using bond enthalpies, for the following reaction:

$H_2(g) + Cl_2(g) \rightarrow 2HCl(g)$

The necessary data are given in Tables 14.1 and 14.2.

Table 14.1

Bonds broken	$\Delta H/\text{kJ mol}^{-1}$
H–H	436
Cl–Cl	243
Total	**679**

Table 14.2

Bonds made	$\Delta H/\text{kJ mol}^{-1}$
H–Cl	−432
H–Cl	−432
Total	**−864**

Solution

Enthalpy change = total bonds broken + total bonds made

$\Delta H = 679 + (-864) = -185 \text{ kJ mol}^{-1}$

Key points

* The enthalpy change can be calculated for a chemical reaction using the equation $E_h = cm\Delta T$.
* Hess's law can be used to calculate the enthalpy change for a chemical reaction.
* Bond enthalpy data can be used to calculate the enthalpy change for a chemical reaction.

Study questions

1 0.05 mol of methane released 45 kJ of energy when burned. Calculate the enthalpy of combustion of methane.

2 12 g of sulfur released 80 kJ of energy when burned. Calculate the enthalpy of combustion of sulfur.

3 An experiment was carried out to determine the energy released when ethanol is burned. Use the data shown to calculate an experimental value for the enthalpy of combustion of ethanol.

Mass of ethanol burner at the start of the experiment	82 g
Mass of ethanol burner at the end of the experiment	81.4 g
Temperature of water at the start of the experiment	23.1 °C
Temperature of water at the end of the experiment	38.3 °C
Volume of water heated	100 cm^3

4 The equation for the enthalpy of formation of ethyne is shown below. Using the enthalpies of combustion of carbon, hydrogen and ethyne, calculate the enthalpy of formation of ethyne.
$$2C(s) + H_2(g) \rightarrow C_2H_2(g)$$

5 Ethene gas can react with hydrogen gas to form ethane by the equation below. Using bond enthalpies, calculate the enthalpy change for this reaction.
$$C_2H_4(g) + H_2(g) \rightarrow C_2H_6(g)$$

6 The equation for the combustion of diborane is shown below.
$$B_2H_6(g) + 3O_2(g) \rightarrow B_2O_3(s) + 3H_2O(l)$$
Calculate the enthalpy of combustion of diborane (B_2H_6) using the following data.

$$2B(s) + 3H_2(g) \rightarrow B_2H_6(g) \qquad \Delta H = 36 \text{ kJ mol}^{-1}$$

$$H_2(g) + \frac{1}{2}O_2(g) \rightarrow H_2O(l) \qquad \Delta H = -286 \text{ kJ mol}^{-1}$$

$$2B(s) + 1\frac{1}{2}O_2(g) \rightarrow B_2O_3(s) \qquad \Delta H = -1274 \text{ kJ mol}^{-1}$$

7 When chlorine gas reacts with methane in the presence of light, a free radical reaction occurs forming chloromethane and hydrogen chloride.
   a) Using bond enthalpies, calculate the enthalpy change for this reaction.
   b) Showing appropriate symbols and formulae, write an equation for the initiation step of this reaction.

Chapter 15
Oxidising and reducing agents

Redox reactions

When zinc metal is added to a solution of copper (II) sulfate, a **redox reaction** takes place.

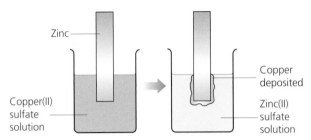

Figure 15.1 An example of a redox reaction

The **electrochemical series** can be used to write ion–electron equations for oxidation and reduction reactions. In the case of the reaction illustrated in Figure 15.1, the zinc metal is higher in the electrochemical series than the copper ions. As a result, the zinc is oxidised and the copper ions are reduced. An overall redox reaction can be written by cancelling the electrons and combining the equations:

Oxidation: $Zn(s) \rightarrow Zn^{2+}(aq) + 2e^-$

Reduction: $Cu^{2+}(aq) + 2e^- \rightarrow Cu(s)$

Redox: $Zn(s) + Cu^{2+}(aq) \rightarrow Zn^{2+}(aq) + Cu(s)$

Zinc is acting as a **reducing agent** since it supplies the electrons which cause the copper ions to be reduced.

Cu^{2+} is acting as an **oxidising agent** since it accepts the electrons from the zinc.

Remember

An oxidising agent is a substance that accepts electrons.

A reducing agent is a substance that donates electrons.

Using electronegativity

Electronegativity values can be used to predict whether a substance will act as an oxidising or reducing agent.

Remember

Reducing agents have low electronegativity values.

Oxidising agents have high electronegativity values.

Most metals have low electronegativity values. They act as reducing agents.

Non-metals have higher electronegativity values. They act as oxidising agents.

For example, the alkali metals readily form positively charged ions. In doing so, they 'lose' electrons to other substances causing them to be reduced. The alkali metals have the lowest electronegativity values of all the elements.

Example

The following question appears in various forms in SQA past papers. This version is taken from the 2007 Higher Paper.

Which of the following is a redox reaction?

A $Mg + 2HCl \rightarrow MgCl_2 + H_2$
B $MgO + 2HCl \rightarrow MgCl_2 + H_2O$
C $MgCO_3 + 2HCl \rightarrow MgCl_2 + H_2O + CO_2$
D $Mg(OH)_2 + 2HCl \rightarrow MgCl_2 + 2H_2O$

These questions are straightforward to solve. Always look for the equation where the metal is changing from an element to a compound or vice versa. For a metal to form a compound it has to form ions, in other words it has to oxidise. In this case, the only answer suitable is A. The magnesium is oxidised to form Mg^{2+} ions. The reduction equation is the formation of hydrogen gas:

$2H^+ + 2e^- \rightarrow H_2$

In all of the other answers, the magnesium is an ion as a reactant and an ion as a product – it does not change.

A similar question type is shown here. This question came from a Higher Chemistry exam paper in 2008.

In which of the following reactions is the hydrogen ion acting as an oxidising agent?

A $Mg + 2HCl \rightarrow MgCl_2 + H_2$
B $NaOH + HNO_3 \rightarrow NaNO_3 + H_2O$
C $CuCO_3 + H_2SO_4 \rightarrow CuSO_4 + H_2O + CO_2$
D $CH_3COONa + HCl \rightarrow NaCl + CH_3COOH$

Again, look for an equation involving a metal changing. The only equation where the metal changes is equation A in which the Mg atom turns into Mg ions; it is oxidised. Thus, the hydrogen ions (from the HCl) must be acting as an oxidising agent.

Compounds as oxidising and reducing agents

In Unit 2 you learned that alcohols could be oxidised using oxidising agents such as acidified potassium dichromate. In such examples, the ion causing the oxidation is the dichromate ion, $Cr_2O_7^{2-}$(aq).

Other compounds can cause oxidation or reduction:
- The permanganate ion (MnO_4^-) is a powerful oxidising agent.
- Carbon monoxide (CO) is a powerful reducing agent.

An examination of the data booklet shows that the dichromate and permanganate ions are located at the bottom of the electrochemical series.

Remember

Elements and compounds at the bottom left of the electrochemical series are strong oxidising agents.

Elements and compounds at the top right of the electrochemical series are strong reducing agents.

Writing redox equations

Simple redox equations can be written for redox reactions provided it is known which substance is being oxidised and which substance is being reduced. In order to combine two ion–electron equations, the number of electrons must be equal. This is shown in the following examples.

Example

Write ion–electron equations and combine them to form a redox equation for the reaction of the permanganate ion with iron (II) ions.

Solution

Since the question states that the reaction is between permanganate and iron (II), the ion–electron equations must start with these ions. Both ion electron equations can be obtained from the ECS:

$$MnO_4^- + 8H^+ + 5e^- \rightarrow Mn^{2+} + 4H_2O$$

The permanganate equation is, therefore, a reduction which means that we are looking for an ion–electron equation for the *oxidation* of iron (II).

$$Fe^{2+} \rightarrow Fe^{3+} + e^-$$

The iron (II) equation must be multiplied by 5 so that the number of electrons lost is equal to the number of electrons gained by the permanganate ion.

$$MnO_4^- + 8H^+ + 5e^- \rightarrow Mn^{2+} + 4H_2O$$
$$5Fe^{2+} \rightarrow 5Fe^{3+} + 5e^-$$
$$\overline{MnO_4^- + 8H^+ + 5Fe^{2+} \rightarrow Mn^{2+} + 4H_2O + 5Fe^{3+}}$$

Writing more complex ion–electron equations

Example

Write an ion–electron equation for the conversion of dichromate into chromium (III) ions.

Solution

Since the ion–electron equation for this reaction is in the data booklet, we will be able to check our answer. The steps for solving these more complex equations are:

1 Check that the main element reacting (not oxygen) is balanced.
2 Add water to balance oxygen atoms.
3 Add H^+ ions to balance the hydrogen atoms.
4 Add electrons to the same side as the H^+ ions so that both sides of the equation have the same charge.

The starting equation is:

$$Cr_2O_7^{2-} \rightarrow Cr^{3+}$$

Step 1: We must double the chromium (III) to balance both sides.

$$Cr_2O_7^{2-} \rightarrow 2Cr^{3+}$$

Step 2: We must add water to the right-hand side to balance the oxygen atoms.

$$Cr_2O_7^{2-} \rightarrow 2Cr^{3+} + 7H_2O$$

Step 3: We must add H^+ ions to the left-hand side to balance the hydrogens.

$$Cr_2O_7^{2-} + 14H^+ \rightarrow 2Cr^{3+} + 7H_2O$$

Step 4: We must add electrons to the left-hand side to ensure the charge is the same on both sides. Since the charge is 12+ on the reactant side and 6+ on the product side, $6e^-$ must be added to the reactant side to give an overall 6+ charge to the reactants. This is the final stage and will give us our solution:

$$Cr_2O_7^{2-} + 14H^+ + 6e^- \rightarrow 2Cr^{3+} + 7H_2O$$

Everyday uses for strong oxidising agents

Hydrogen peroxide is a highly effective bleach as it is able to break down coloured compounds. It is found in teeth-whitening products and hair products. Like many oxidising agents, hydrogen peroxide is also an effective antiseptic as it can kill bacteria and fungi and destroy viruses. Potassium permanganate is also used for its antiseptic properties and is commonly used in aquaria to destroy the bacteria and fungi that can infect fish.

Key points

* Ion–electron equations can be written for reactions and such equations can be combined to form redox equations.
* Metals tend to act as reducing agents as they readily lose electrons.
* Non-metals tend to act as oxidising agents as they readily gain electrons.
* The electronegativity scale can be used to assess whether a substance is likely to be an oxidising or reducing agent. Reducing agents have low electronegativity values. Oxidising agents have high electronegativity values.
* Strong oxidising agents such as hydrogen peroxide and potassium permanganate are powerful antiseptics.

Study questions

1 Magnesium reacts with silver (I) ions to form silver and a solution of magnesium ions.
   a) Write ion–electron equations for the oxidation and reduction reactions taking place.
   b) Combine the equations to form a redox equation.
   c) Identify the oxidising agent and the reducing agent.

2 Place the following substances in order of their ability to act as an oxidising agent (strongest to weakest): calcium, chlorine, fluorine and sodium.

3 Complete the ion–electron equations for the following:
   a) $SO_3^{2-} \rightarrow SO_4^{2-}$
   b) $NO_3^- \rightarrow NO$
   c) $H_2O_2 \rightarrow O_2$
   d) $VO_3^- \rightarrow V^{2+}$

4 In which reaction is hydrogen gas acting as a reducing agent?

   A $H_2 + \dfrac{1}{2}O_2 \rightarrow H_2O$

   B $H_2 + PbO \rightarrow Pb + H_2O$
   C $H_2 + 2Li \rightarrow 2LiH$
   D $H_2 + C_4H_8 \rightarrow C_4H_{10}$

5 Carbon monoxide can be used to extract metals from their ores. For example, when iron (III) oxide is reacted with carbon monoxide, iron metal and carbon dioxide are formed.
   a) Write a balanced chemical equation for this reaction.
   b) Write an ion–electron equation for iron (III) forming iron metal.
   c) Hence, state whether carbon monoxide is acting as an oxidising or reducing agent.

Chromatography

Chromatography is used to separate the components in a mixture. Figure 16.1 shows an example of paper chromatography.

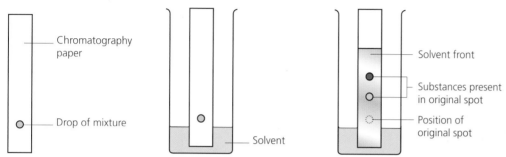

Figure 16.1 Paper chromatography

In the example shown in Figure 16.1, the original mixture separates into two components. Separation usually depends on:

- the size of the molecules
- the polarity of the molecules.

A component can often be identified by how far it has travelled. For example, if the paper chromatography shown in Figure 16.1 was run using a non-polar solvent such as hexane, non-polar components would be attracted to the hexane and would be expected to travel further up the paper than polar components. In this case, it would be deduced that the red spot is less polar than the yellow spot.

In other forms of chromatography such as **gas liquid chromatography** (**GLC**), the results of the experiment are shown graphically as in Figure 16.2.

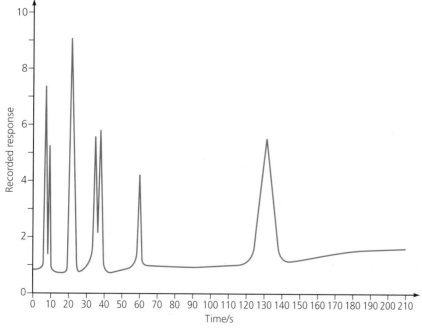

Figure 16.2 A graph from a GLC (chromatogram)

Fig 16.2 shows the **retention time** for each component: peaks with a short time have gone through the chromatography column quickly. Again, this is related to the size and/or the polarity of the components. For example, the peak at 130 s represents the component with the longest retention time, i.e. the component that has taken the longest time to travel through the column. This could be the biggest molecule.

Example

In an arson investigation, a chromatogram was obtained from a sample of fresh petrol and compared to a chromatogram obtained from a partially evaporated petrol sample from a piece of fabric.

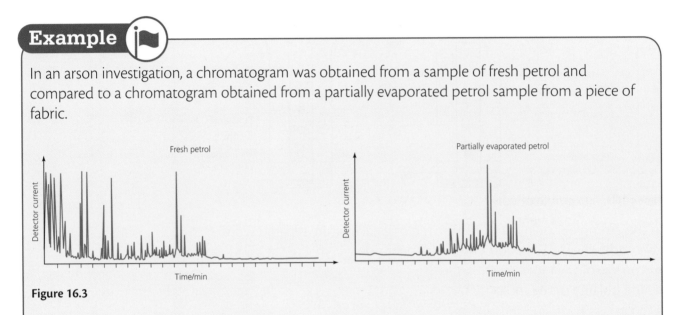

Figure 16.3

Explain how these chromatograms show that large molecules have longer retention times than small molecules in this type of chromatography.

Solution

Small molecules would be expected to evaporate more quickly than larger molecules. Since the chromatogram for the partially evaporated petrol shows an absence of peaks with short retention times, this would suggest that small molecules have a short retention time and, therefore, large molecules have a longer retention time.

Volumetric analysis

Volumetric analysis involves using a solution of known concentration to determine the concentration of an unknown solution. This is usually done using titrations which require the use of pipettes, burettes, **indicators** and standard flasks.

A solution of known concentration is known as a **standard solution**. The steps required to make a standard solution are shown in Figure 16.4.

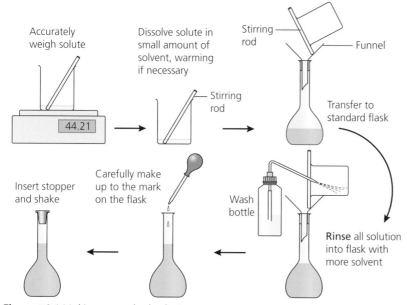

Figure 16.4 Making a standard solution

A common example of volumetric analysis is an *acid–alkali titration*. Consider an experiment where a known concentration of hydrochloric acid is titrated with an unknown concentration of sodium hydroxide solution.

By adding a fixed volume of the alkali into a flask, along with a suitable indicator, the volume of acid required to completely neutralise the alkali can be determined (Figure 16.5). The acid is added from the burette until the **end-point** is reached, as shown by the indicator changing colour.

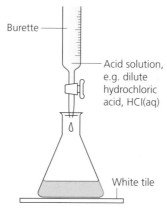

Figure 16.5 Determining the concentration of an alkali by titrating with an acid of known concentration

The volume of acid required to reach this end-point can be read from the burette. Once this volume is known, the number of moles of acid can be calculated since its concentration is already known. Now, a balanced chemical equation can be used to find out the unknown concentration of the alkali. This is illustrated by the following two examples.

Example

25 cm³ of sodium hydroxide solution was added to a flask and titrated with 0.1 mol l⁻¹ hydrochloric acid. The volume of hydrochloric acid required to neutralise the sodium hydroxide was found to be 10.0 cm³. Use these results to calculate the concentration of the sodium hydroxide solution.

Solution

$HCl(aq) + NaOH(aq) \rightarrow NaCl(aq) + H_2O(l)$

Table 16.1

	HCl(aq)	NaOH(aq)
Mole ratio	1	1
Concentration, C	$0.1\,mol\,l^{-1}$	?
Volume, V	$10\,cm^3$	$25\,cm^3$

From the information given in Table 16.1, the number of moles of hydrochloric acid reacting can be calculated using the equation moles = CV, where V is measured in litres.

Moles $= 0.1 \times 0.01 = 0.001$

From the mole ratio, 1 mole of HCl reacts with 1 mole of NaOH.

Thus, 0.001 moles of HCl would react with 0.001 moles of NaOH.

Concentration of NaOH $= \frac{moles}{volume} = \frac{0.001}{0.025} = 0.04\,mol\,l^{-1}$

Example

In a titration, it was found that $10\,cm^3$ of potassium hydroxide was neutralised by $0.05\,mol\,l^{-1}$ sulfuric acid. The volumes of sulfuric acid used in the titration are recorded in Table 16.2.

Table 16.2

Titration	Volume of $0.05\,mol\,l^{-1}$ sulfuric acid/cm^3
1	18.0
2	17.4
3	17.3

Calculate the concentration of the potassium hydroxide given that potassium hydroxide reacts with sulfuric acid according to the equation shown.

$2KOH(aq) + H_2SO_4(aq) \rightarrow K_2SO_4(aq) + 2H_2O(l)$

Solution

Average volume of sulfuric acid $= \frac{17.3 + 17.4}{2} = 17.35\,cm^3$

(See Appendix 1 for more details on calculating the average and eliminating rogue data.)

Number of moles of sulfuric acid reacting $= CV = 0.05 \times 0.01735 = 0.00087$

According to the equation, 1 mole of H_2SO_4 reacts with 2 moles of KOH.

Thus, 0.00087 moles of H_2SO_4 will react with 0.0017 moles of KOH.

Concentration of KOH $= \frac{moles}{volume} = \frac{0.0017}{0.01} = 0.17\,mol\,l^{-1}$

Redox titrations

The concept of volumetric titrations can be applied to redox reactions. For example, a solution of potassium permanganate of known concentration can be used to determine the quantity of iron in iron tablets. The steps for this experiment are shown in Figure 16.6.

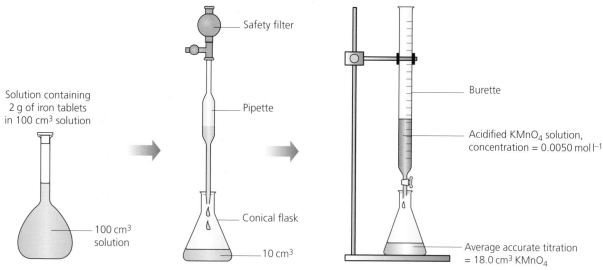

Figure 16.6 Determining the mass of iron in an iron tablet by volumetric titration

The redox reaction for this experiment is:

$$MnO_4^- + 8H^+ + 5e^- \rightarrow Mn^{2+} + 4H_2O$$
$$5Fe^{2+} \rightarrow 5Fe^{3+} + 5e^-$$

$$MnO_4^- + 8H^+ + 5Fe^{2+} \rightarrow Mn^{2+} + 4H_2O + 5Fe^{3+}$$

In other words, 1 mole of potassium permanganate will react with 5 moles of iron (II) ions.

From the experiment shown, the moles of permanganate required can be calculated:

Moles = $CV = 0.005 \times 0.018 = 9 \times 10^{-5}$ moles

Moles of $Fe^{2+} = 5 \times$ moles of permanganate = $5 \times (9 \times 10^{-5}) = 0.00045$ moles

In other words, number of moles of Fe^{2+} present in $10\,cm^3$ solution = 0.00045 moles

Number of moles of Fe^{2+} present in $100\,cm^3$ solution = 0.0045 moles

Mass of iron present = moles $\times$ gfm = $0.0045 \times 55.8 = 0.25\,g$

Example

To determine the concentration of an iron (II) sulfate solution by titration with a potassium permanganate solution of known concentration

$20\,cm^3$ of iron (II) sulfate solution is transferred by pipette to a conical flask and excess dilute sulfuric acid is added. Potassium permanganate solution ($0.02\,mol\,l^{-1}$) is added from the burette until the contents of the flask just turn from colourless to purple, initial and final burette readings being noted. The titration is repeated to obtain concordant titres. ⇨

Since the permanganate solution is so strongly coloured compared to the other solutions, the reaction is self-indicating and the change at the end-point from colourless to purple is quite sharp.

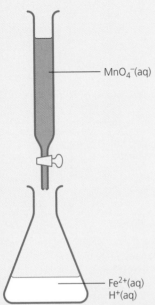

— $MnO_4^-(aq)$

— $Fe^{2+}(aq)$
$H^+(aq)$

Figure 16.7 The redox titration between permanganate and iron (II) is an example of a self-indicating reaction since the purple colour of permanganate appears once all the iron (II) ions have reacted.

Calculate the concentration of an iron (II) sulfate solution given that 20.0 cm³ of it reacted with 24.0 cm³ of 0.02 mol l⁻¹ potassium permanganate solution. The redox equation for the reaction is:

$$MnO_4^- + 8H^+ + 5Fe^{2+} \rightarrow 5Fe^{3+} + Mn^{2+} + 4H_2O$$

Solution

According to the equation, 1 mole of MnO_4^- oxidises 5 moles of Fe^{2+}.

Number of moles of MnO_4^- used $= CV = 0.02 \times 0.024 = 4.8 \times 10^{-4}$

Hence, number of moles of Fe^{2+} present $= 5 \times 4.8 \times 10^{-4} = 2.4 \times 10^{-3}$

This is contained in 20 cm³, i.e. 0.02 litres.

Hence, concentration of $Fe^{2+}(aq)$, $C = \frac{2.4 \times 10^{-3}}{0.02} = 0.12$ mol l⁻¹

Since 1 mole $FeSO_4(aq)$ contains 1 mole of $Fe^{2+}(aq)$, the concentration of $FeSO_4(aq) = 0.12$ mol l⁻¹.

Redox titrations, such as the permanganate/iron titration, are said to be self-indicating; there is no need for an indicator as the purple permanganate colour is used to judge the end-point. The solution will remain colourless provided there are iron (II) ions to react with the purple permanganate ions. Once all of the iron (II) ions have reacted, the end-point – the purple colour – will appear.

Hint & tips

When solving any volumetric/redox titration questions, you should look for
a) a balanced chemical equation
b) information on concentration and volume.
You will always be able to calculate the number of moles of one substance using moles = CV. You can then use the mole ratio from the equation to calculate the number of moles of the 'unknown' substance. Dividing this by the volume shown will allow you to work out a concentration.

Key points

* A standard solution is a solution of accurately known concentration.
* The end-point of a titration is the point at which the reaction is just complete.
* An indicator is a substance which changes colour at the end-point.
* Some titrations are self-indicating.
* Redox titrations can be used to determine the concentration of a substance.

Study questions ?

1 The concentration of an iodine solution was determined by a redox titration. $10\,cm^3$ of a standard sodium sulfite solution, $0.1\,mol\,l^{-1}$, was transferred into a conical flask. It was found that $24.3\,cm^3$ of iodine was required to reach the end-point of the titration. The redox equation for the reaction is

$$SO_3^{2-} + I_2 + H_2O \rightarrow 2I^- + SO_4^{2-} + 2H^+$$

 a) Name the piece of apparatus used to transfer the sodium sulfite solution into the flask accurately.
 b) Name the piece of equipment used to determine the volume of iodine required.
 c) Calculate the concentration of the iodine solution.

2 Vitamin C, $C_6H_8O_6$, reacts with iodine according to the following redox equation

$$C_6H_8O_6 + I_2 \rightarrow C_6H_6O_6 + 2H^+$$

 In an experiment to determine the mass of vitamin C in a fruit juice, the following procedure was used.

 $80\,cm^3$ of fruit juice was measured accurately and transferred to a $200\,cm^3$ standard flask. The standard flask was made up to the mark with water. $20\,cm^3$ portions of this solution were added to a flask and titrated with iodine, using starch as the indicator. The results of the titration with $0.01\,mol\,l^{-1}$ iodine solution are shown in Table 16.3.

 Table 16.3

Experiment	Volume of iodine/cm³
1	12.5
2	12.1
3	12.0

 a) Calculate the average volume of iodine used.
 b) Suggest how the $20\,cm^3$ portion of juice was added to the flask.
 c) Calculate the number of moles of iodine reacting with the $20\,cm^3$ juice sample.
 d) Calculate the mass of vitamin C present in the original $80\,cm^3$ of juice.

3 Mixtures of amino acids can be separated using paper chromatography. On a chromatogram, the retention factor, R_f, for a substance can be a useful method of identifying the substance. $\Rightarrow$

$$R_f = \frac{\text{distance moved by spot}}{\text{distance moved by solvent}}$$

a) A solution containing a mixture of four amino acids was applied to a piece of chromatography paper that was then placed in solvent 1. Chromatogram 1 is shown in Figure 16.8.

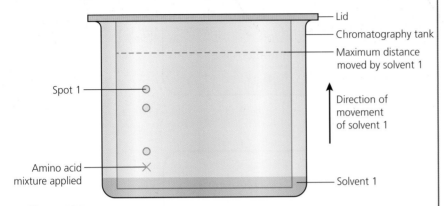

Figure 16.8

Amino acid	R_f (solvent 1)
Alanine	0.51
Arginine	0.16
Threonine	0.51
Tyrosine	0.68

The retention factors for the amino acids in solvent 1 are shown in the table. Identify the amino acid that corresponds to spot 1 on the chromatogram.

b) The chromatogram was dried, rotated through 90° and then placed in solvent 2. Chromatogram 2 is shown in Figure 16.9.

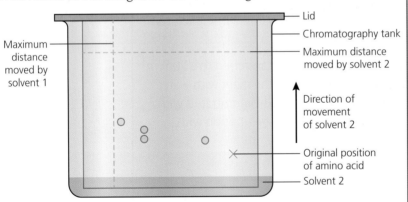

Figure 16.9

Amino acid	R_f (solvent 2)
Alanine	0.21
Arginine	0.21
Threonine	0.34
Tyrosine	0.43

The retention factors for the amino acids in solvent 2 are shown in the table. Draw a circle around the spot on a copy of chromatogram 2 that corresponds to the amino acid alanine.

c) Explain why only three spots are present in chromatogram 1 while four spots are present in chromatogram 2.

Additional features of the Higher Chemistry exam

Numeracy

The Higher Chemistry exam will contain several questions that test your numeracy skills. Some of these questions have been covered in earlier chapters, such as calculating reaction rates, enthalpy changes and percentage yield. Other questions will ask you to 'scale up' or 'scale down' as this is a skill that is used by practising scientists in their day to day job.

Being able to deal with proportion is key to answering numeracy questions in chemistry. A common layout is shown in the examples below. In all cases, the unknown (what you are being asked to calculate) should be put on the right-hand side.

Example

1.2 g of methane burned to produce 52 kJ of energy. Calculate the enthalpy of combustion of methane.

Solution

This is really a proportion question. You have to understand that the enthalpy of combustion is the energy released when 1 mole of a substance is burned completely and that 1 mole of methane is the gram formula mass, 16 g.

Step 1: State a relationship.

$$\text{mass} \rightarrow \text{energy}$$
$$1.2 \text{ g} \rightarrow 52 \text{ kJ}$$

(Note that energy is placed on the right-hand side as we want to calculate the energy.)

Step 2: Scale to 1.

$$1 \text{ g} \rightarrow \frac{52}{1.2} = 43.3 \text{ kJ}$$

Step 3: Calculate for the mass you are asked for in the question.

$$16 \text{ g} \rightarrow 16 \times 43.3 = 693.3$$

Finally, answer the question, giving the correct units as necessary:

The ΔH combustion for methane = −693.3 kJ mol⁻¹.

Example

A 10 kg batch of NaOH(s) cost £43. Calculate the cost for 4 g of NaOH(s).

Solution

Following the steps outlined in the first example:

$$mass \rightarrow cost$$
$$10\,000\,g \rightarrow £43$$
$$1\,g \rightarrow \frac{43}{10\,000} = 4.3 \times 10^{-3}$$
$$4\,g \rightarrow 4 \times (4.3 \times 10^{-3}) = £0.017 = 17p$$

Therefore, 4 g of NaOH(s) would cost 17p.

Example

A 100 ml bottle of children's paracetamol costs £3.85. The ingredients label states that each 5 ml dose contains 120 mg of paracetamol. Calculate the cost per mg of paracetamol.

Solution

$$volume \rightarrow mass$$
$$5\,ml \rightarrow 120\,mg$$
$$1\,ml \rightarrow 24\,mg$$
$$100\,ml \rightarrow 2400\,mg$$

i.e. 1 bottle contains 2400 mg of paracetamol

$$mass \rightarrow cost$$
$$2400\,mg \rightarrow £3.85$$
$$1\,mg \rightarrow £0.0016$$

Paracetamol costs £0.0016 per mg.

Example

Theobromine, a compound present in chocolate, can cause illness in dogs and cats. To decide if treatment is necessary, vets must calculate the mass of theobromine consumed.

1.0 g of chocolate contains 1.4 mg of theobromine.

Calculate the mass, in mg, of theobromine in a 17 g biscuit of which 28% is chocolate.

Solution

A 17 g biscuit contains 28% chocolate, i.e. mass of chocolate = 28% of 17 = 0.28 × 17 = 4.76 g

⇨
mass of chocolate → mass of theobromine

$$1.0\,g → 1.4\,mg$$
$$4.76\,g → 4.76 × 1.4 = 6.66\,mg$$

There is 6.66 mg of theobromine in the biscuit.

Example

The maximum safe dose of lidocaine for an adult is 4.5 mg of lidocaine per kg of body mass.

1.0 cm³ of lidocaine solution contains 10 mg of lidocaine.

Calculate the maximum volume of lidocaine solution that could be given to a 70 kg adult.

Solution

mass of adult → mass of lidocaine

$$1\,kg → 4.5\,mg$$
$$70\,kg → 315\,mg$$

i.e. the maximum mass of lidocaine that can be given is 315 mg

mass of lidocaine → volume of solution

$$1\,mg → 0.1\,cm^3$$
$$10\,mg → 1.0\,cm^3$$
$$315\,mg → 31.5\,cm^3$$

A maximum volume of 31.5 cm³ can be given to the adult.

Open-ended questions

Real-life chemistry problems rarely have a fixed answer. In the Higher exam, you will encounter questions that are open-ended; there is more than one 'correct' answer. To tackle these, look at the example shown and the marking scheme.

Example

Cooking involves many chemical reactions. Proteins, fats, oils and esters are some examples of compounds found in food. A chemist suggested that cooking food could change compounds from being fat-soluble to water-soluble.

Use your knowledge of chemistry to comment on the accuracy of this statement.

Marking scheme

0 marks: The student has demonstrated no understanding of the chemistry involved. There is no evidence that the student has recognised the area of chemistry involved or has given any statement of a relevant chemistry principle. This mark would also be given when the student merely restates the chemistry given in the question. ⇨

1 mark: The student has demonstrated a limited understanding of the chemistry involved. The candidate has made some statement(s) which is/are relevant to the situation, showing that at least a little of the chemistry within the problem is understood.

2 marks: The student has demonstrated a reasonable understanding of the chemistry involved. The student makes some statement(s) which is/are relevant to the situation, showing that the problem is understood.

3 marks: The maximum available mark would be awarded to a student who has demonstrated a good understanding of the chemistry involved. The student shows a good comprehension of the chemistry of the situation and has provided a logically correct answer to the question posed. This type of response might include a statement of the principles involved, a relationship or an equation, and the application of these to respond to the problem. This does not mean the answer has to be what might be termed an 'excellent' answer or a 'complete' one.

Author's suggested solution

To tackle a question like this, focus on the key chemical words and think about the chemistry you know. What chemical reactions do you know that involve proteins, fats, oils and esters? Can you relate this to solubility?

Proteins – Long-chain molecules linked by hydrogen bonding. Perhaps the proteins in food are insoluble as the chains are attracted to themselves. Cooking could cause the protein chains to untwist (breaking the hydrogen bonds) making them more likely to attract water to the exposed peptide links. In addition, cooking could cause the protein to hydrolyse to produce amino acids. Amino acids contain the polar amine group ($-NH_2$) and carboxyl group ($-COOH$); both can form hydrogen bonds to water, therefore the amino acids can dissolve in water.

Fats and oils – Insoluble in water as they are mainly large hydrocarbon structures. Fats and oils can hydrolyse to produce glycerol and fatty acids. Glycerol has three $-OH$ groups so it could H-bond to water molecules and dissolve. Fatty acids contain a polar head (the carboxyl group, $-COOH$) which is water soluble.

Esters – Non-polar and insoluble. Heating could hydrolyse the ester group producing an alcohol and carboxylic acid. Both of these molecules are polar and would dissolve in water.

A good answer for this question would not have to contain all of the above. Indeed, it could focus on one molecule but give lots of detail. It is also a good idea to illustrate your answer with diagrams – you could show typical structures and explain how they can bond to water. If it enhances your answer by showing the examiner that you understand the chemistry, include it!

Researching chemistry

As part of your Higher Chemistry experience, you should have had plenty of practice carrying out experiments using standard lab equipment and evaluating your experimental results. In the Higher exam, you are expected to be familiar with the techniques listed in Table AP1.1 and the apparatus listed in Table AP1.2.

Table AP1.1 Some common lab techniques

Distillation
Filtration
Methods for collecting a gas: over water or using a gas syringe
Safe heating methods: using a Bunsen, water bath or heating mantle
Titration
Use of a balance

Table AP1.2 Some items of laboratory apparatus

Beaker	Dropper	Pipette filler
Boiling tube	Evaporating basin	Test tubes
Burette	Funnel	Thermometer
Conical flask	Measuring cylinder	Volumetric flask
Delivery tubes	Pipette	

You should ensure you are familiar with the techniques and apparatus. The following general points are worth noting.

Pipettes and burettes

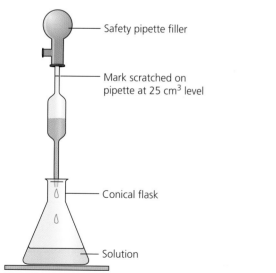

Figure AP1.1 A pipette with safety filler

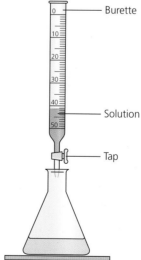

Figure AP1.2 A burette

A pipette is more accurate than a measuring cylinder for measuring fixed volumes of liquid. A burette can be used to measure non-standard volumes of liquid.

Example

Suggest the best piece of apparatus to measure

a) 20 cm³ of solution

b) 23.5 cm³ of solution.

Solution

a) pipette

b) burette

Standard flasks and standard solutions

A standard flask is used to make up a standard solution – a solution of known concentration. This is done by dissolving a known mass of solute in water and transferring to the standard flask with rinsings. Finally, the standard flask is made up to the mark with water.

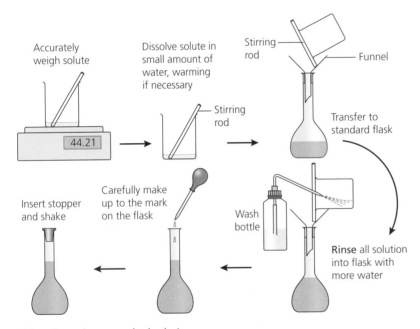

Figure AP1.3 Preparing a standard solution

Collecting a gas

The two common methods for collecting gases are shown in Figures AP1.4 and AP1.5. The gas syringe can be used for collecting both soluble and insoluble gases and has the advantage that it can measure the volume of gas produced. Collecting a gas by bubbling through water is only appropriate if the gas is **insoluble** in water and can only be used to measure the volume if the collecting vessel is graduated, such as an upturned measuring cylinder.

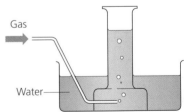

Figure AP1.4 Collecting an **insoluble** gas

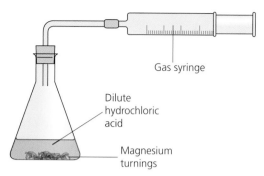

Gas syringe

Dilute
hydrochloric
acid

Magnesium
turnings

Figure AP1.5 Collecting and measuring a gas using a gas syringe

Experimental data

From your experience working with experimental data, you should know how to calculate averages, how to eliminate **rogue data**, how to draw graphs (scatter and best fit line/curve) and how to interpret graphs.

It is common in Higher exams to be presented with titration data such as that shown in Table AP1.3.

Table AP1.3

Titration	Volume of solution/cm³
1	26.0
2	24.1
3	39.0
4	24.2
5	24.8

Result 1 is a rough titration which is not accurate.

Results 2 and 4 could be used to calculate an average volume (= 24.15 cm³).

Result 3 is a rogue result and should be ignored.

Result 5 cannot be used to calculate the average volume as it is too far from 24.1 and 24.2 – it is not accurate.

Study questions

1 45 cm³ of a solution could be most accurately measured out using a
   A 50 cm³ beaker
   B 50 cm³ burette
   C 50 cm³ pipette
   D 50 cm³ measuring cylinder.

2 Aluminium carbonate can be produced by the following reaction

$2AlCl_3(aq) + 3K_2CO_3(aq) \rightarrow Al_2(CO_3)_3(s) + 6KCl(aq)$

   The most suitable method for obtaining a sample of the aluminium carbonate is
   A collection over water
   B distillation
   C evaporation
   D filtration.

3 The flavour and texture of chocolate comes from a blend of compounds. Using your knowledge of chemistry, describe how you could show that there are ionic compounds and covalent compounds present in chocolate.

4 A student analysed a local water supply to determine fluoride and nitrite ion levels.

a) The concentration of fluoride ions in water was determined by adding a red coloured compound that absorbs light to the water samples. The fluoride ions reacted with the red compound to produce a colourless compound. Higher concentrations of fluoride ions produce less coloured solutions which absorb less light. The student initially prepared a standard solution of sodium fluoride with fluoride ion concentration of 100 mg l^{-1}.

   i. State what is meant by the term standard solution.

   ii. Describe how the standard solution is prepared from a weighed sample of sodium fluoride.

   iii. Explain why the student should use distilled or deionised water rather than tap water when preparing the standard solution.

b) The student prepared a series of standard solutions of fluoride ions and reacted each with a sample of the red compound. The light absorbance of each solution was measured and the results graphed. Determine the concentration of fluoride ions in a solution with absorbance 0.012.

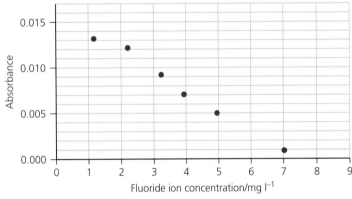

Figure AP1.6

c) The concentration of nitrite ions in the water supply was determined by titrating water samples with acidified permanganate solutions. An average of 21.6 cm³ of 0.015 mol l⁻¹ acidified permanganate solution was required to react completely with the nitrite ions in a 25.0 cm³ sample of water. The equation for the reaction taking place is

$$2MnO_4^-(aq) + 5NO_2^-(aq) + 6H^+(aq) \rightarrow 2Mn^{2+}(aq) + 5NO_3^-(aq) + 3H_2O(l)$$

Calculate the nitrite ion concentration, in mol l⁻¹, in the water. Show your working clearly.

5 In a combustion chamber, cyanogen gas burns to form a mixture of carbon dioxide and nitrogen.

$$C_2N_2(g) + 2O_2(g) \rightarrow 2CO_2(g) + N_2(g)$$

Carbon dioxide can be removed by passing the gas mixture through sodium hydroxide solution. Copy and complete the diagram to show how carbon dioxide can be removed from the products and the volume of nitrogen gas measured.

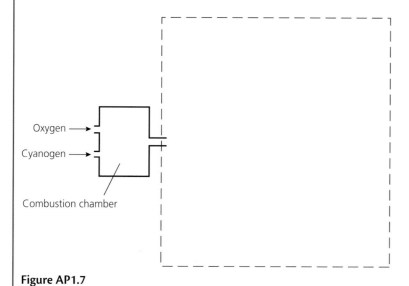

Figure AP1.7

Appendix 2

1 Controlling the rate

1 D
2 A
3 a) B **b)** A **c)** C **d)** B **e)** C
4 $0.0015\,mol\,l^{-1}\,min^{-1}$
5 C
6 a)

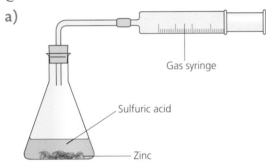

Gas syringe

Sulfuric acid

Zinc

b) i. B **ii.** C **iii.** A **iv.** D

2 Structure and bonding in the first 20 elements

1 a) e **b)** b **c)** d **d)** a
2 a) To melt silicon, strong covalent bonds must be broken since carbon exists as a covalent network. This requires a lot of energy hence the melting point is very high. Nitrogen molecules are attracted to each other by weak London dispersion forces. As these forces are weak, not as much energy is required to overcome these attractions. Therefore, the melting point of nitrogen is much lower than that of silicon.

b) There are many more electrons in a sulfur molecule (S_8) than in a chlorine molecule (Cl_2). The London dispersion forces are therefore stronger between sulfur molecules than between chlorine molecules. Consequently, it takes a lot more energy to break apart the forces of attraction between sulfur molecules than it does to break the forces of attraction between chlorine molecules. Hence, S has a higher melting point.

c) Melting potassium (K) requires breaking apart the strong metallic bonds in K. Melting argon (Ar) requires overcoming the weak London dispersion forces. Since it takes more energy to break the stronger metallic bonds, K has a higher melting point.

3 C
4 C
5 C
6 **a)** Monatomic gas: He, Ne or Ar; Covalent network solid: B, C or Si;
Discrete covalent molecular gas: N, O, F or Cl; Discrete covalent
molecular solid: S or P
  b) They have delocalised electrons.

3 Trends in the Periodic Table

1 C
2 C
3 C
4 B
5 **a) i.** Nuclear charge increases causing the outer electrons to be more
strongly attracted. It therefore takes more energy to remove the
outer electrons as you go across the period.
  ii. $Cl(g) \rightarrow Cl^+(g) + e^-$
  b) Argon does not readily form bonds.
6 **a)** P^{3-} has an extra occupied energy level compared to the aluminium ion.
  b) The calcium ion has a higher nuclear charge compared to the
phosphorus ion, so electrons are pulled closer to the nucleus,
making the calcium ion smaller than the phosphorus ion.

4 Bonding

1 C
2 D
3 B
4 C
5 C
6 A
7 As the molecules increase in size, the boiling points increase. This is
because as the molecules increase in size they have more electrons, so
the strength of LDF between molecules increases. Therefore, it takes
more energy to overcome the LDF and so the bp increases.
8 **a)** These compounds have hydrogen bonding between their
molecules which is much stronger than the LDF or pdp–pdp
interactions that occur between the other molecules in the graph.
Consequently, these molecules have much higher melting points
as more energy is required to overcome the stronger H bonds
between molecules.
  b) i. PH_3 – Both atoms have the same electronegativity value so this
is an example of a non-polar molecule. The bonding between
molecules will be London dispersion forces.
  ii. H_2S – There is a difference in electronegativity values. Pdp–pdp
interactions will occur between molecules.
9 As there is a difference in electronegativity between H and S, the
bond between H and S is polar. Overall, H_2S is a polar molecule.
Consequently, pdp–pdp interactions occur between hydrogen

sulfide molecules. These attractions must be relatively weak if the compound is a gas at room temperature as this suggests that at room temperature, enough energy is supplied to overcome the attractions between molecules.

10 a) This statement is wrong as it suggests that covalent bonds are broken when covalent molecular compounds melt/boil. (This only occurs for covalent network compounds which have very high melting and boiling points, causing them to be solid at room temperature.) It is, in fact, intermolecular forces that have to be broken when covalent compounds are melted or boiled. As these forces are usually weaker than ionic bonds, covalent molecules usually have lower melting and boiling points.

b) Ionic formula refers to the ratio of ions in the lattice. In other words, there is one magnesium ion for every two chloride ions. In the lattice, the magnesium ion is likely to be surrounded by more than two chloride ions. Overall, the ratio will be 1:2.

5 Esters, fats and oils

1 a)

b)

c)

2 a) –OH

b)

c)

3 a) Butyl methanoate

b) Propyl pentanoate

4 a) Methanol and butanoic acid

b) Ethanol and propanoic acid

c) Methanol and ethanoic acid

5 a) Condensation

b) Hydrolysis

6 A

7 B

8 a) Vitamin C is a polar molecule as it contains lots of polar –OH groups. As a result, water can hydrogen bond to the –OH groups allowing it to dissolve vitamin C.

b) Vitamin A is non-polar. It will not be attracted to polar water molecules but will be attracted to non-polar fat molecules (by using London dispersion forces).

9 Oils are liquids at room temperature as they have a high degree of unsaturation. This means that they have an irregular structure which does not allow the oil molecules to pack close together. Consequently, the molecules are not very strongly attracted to each other. Fat molecules have a high degree of saturation, giving them a regular structure which allows them to pack close together. Consequently, the molecules are more strongly attracted to each other and require more energy to pull them apart.

10 a) This molecule is a monoglyceride as it has only one ester link (OR only one –OH group has been used to join to a fatty/carboxylic acid).

   b) The long-chain hydrocarbon

6 Proteins

1 C

2 B

3 D

4 B

5 C

6 a)

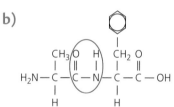

   b)

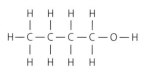

7 Oxidation and the chemistry of cooking

1 D

2 F

3 A

4 B

5 C and E

6 B

7 In addition to the –OH group which is present in both molecules, vanillin has an aldehyde group. The aldehyde group is polar ($\delta+$ C and $\delta-$ O), which will allow it to bond to polar water molecules. In eugenol, the aldehyde group is not present; it has been replaced by a hydrocarbon, which is non-polar and therefore insoluble in water.

8 a) Collagen is a protein. Heating the protein will cause it to denature.

   b) Amino acids

9 a) Hexanoic acid

   b) 2,3-Dimethylpentanoic acid

10 a) Butan-1-ol

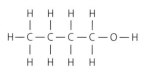

Butan-1,3-diol

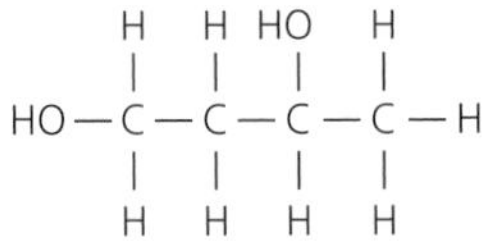

b) Butan-1,3-diol has two hydroxyl groups which allows it to form more hydrogen bonds between molecules. Consequently, more energy has to be supplied to break the hydrogen bonds between butan-1,3-diol molecules and so the boiling point is higher.

8 Soaps, detergents and emulsions

1 C

2 B

3 a)

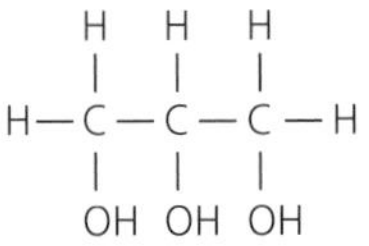

b) The long hydrocarbon chain is non-polar. This can attract non-polar/oily compounds. The –OH groups are polar. These can attract polar/water soluble compounds.

4 a) The circled part represents the non-polar/hydrophobic part of the detergent.

b) The non-polar chain can dissolve in the stain causing the stain to be covered in negative charges. The polar 'head' will not dissolve in the stain and, as a result, the negative charges from the polar heads will repel causing the stain to be broken up into globules of grease. These globules are now water soluble as water molecules can bond to the negative charges.

9 Fragrances

1 a)

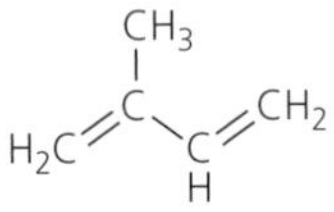

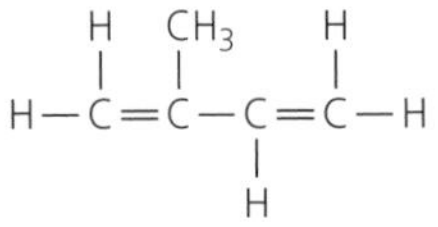

b) 3

2 You could react both compounds with bromine solution. Assuming you had an equal concentration of each, squalene would require double the volume of bromine solution as it has twice as many double bonds per molecule.

3 a) Attempt to oxidise both with Fehling's, Tollen's or acidified dichromate. Citral would oxidise (resulting in a colour change) whereas menthone would not oxidise. (Citral is an aldehyde; menthone is a ketone.)

b)

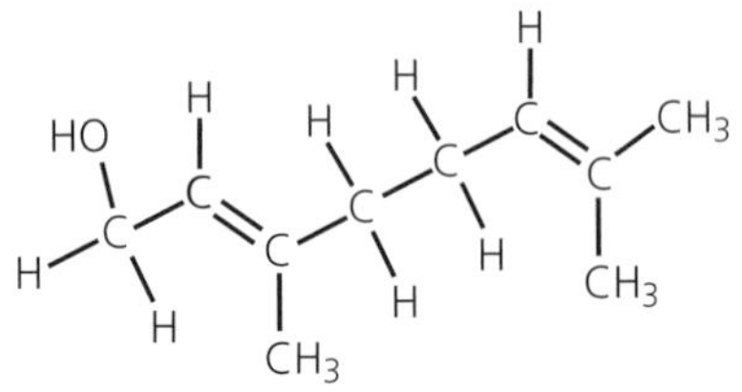

4 C

5 B

6 A

7 **a)** Limonene is completely non-polar. Geraniol contains the polar hydroxyl group. The intermolecular bonding between geraniol molecules (H bonding) is stronger than the intermolecular bonding between limonene molecules (London dispersion forces).

   b) i. Aldehydes

   ii.

$$H_3C-(CH_2)_8-\overset{\overset{\displaystyle CH_3}{|}}{\underset{\underset{\displaystyle H}{|}}{C}}-\overset{\overset{\displaystyle O}{\|}}{C}-OH$$

10 Skin care

1 **a)** A

   b) B and D

   c) C

2 It can react with radicals to form stable molecules.

11 Getting the most from reactants

1 **a)** Sulfur dioxide is a toxic gas. In addition, it can react with water to produce sulfuric acid which contributes to acid rain.

   b) The sulfur dioxide and water could be used in step 1. The oxygen could be sold as a by-product or used in another reaction.

   c) $H_2O \rightarrow H_2 + \frac{1}{2}O_2$

2 **a)** 300 tonnes

   b) A line from the box containing ammonia/carbon dioxide (coming from the separator) back to the reactors.

12 Calculations from equations

1 18 g

2 50 cm^3

3 0.91 g

4 18 g

5 6.82 g

6 **a)** 0.0357 mol CaO and 0.025 mol of H_2SO_4, therefore CaO is in excess as the reactant ratio is 1 : 1

   b) 3.4 g

7 1.2 litres

8 7.77 litres

9 100 cm^3 oxygen, 300 cm^3 CO_2 and 400 cm^3 H_2O

10 8 litres

11 **a)** Methanal

   b) Condensation

   c) 87.4%

   d) 67.8%

12 A
13 a) It is polar/has H bonding
   b) i. Methyl methanoate
      ii. 58%
      iii. 7.38 kg

13 Equilibria

1 C
2 C
3 a) KOH(aq) is a source of OH^- ions. These react with H^+ ions to form water, thus removing the H^+ ions from the solution. The equilibrium will adjust to this change by shifting to the left, which results in more yellow $2CrO_4^{2-}$ being produced.
   b) Sulfuric acid is a source of H^+ ions. An excess of H^+ ions causes the equilibrium to shift to the right, which results in more $Cr_2O_7^{2-}$ (orange) and H_2O being produced.
4 a) i. The reaction will speed up.
      ii. The equilibrium will shift to the left causing the yield of ammonia to decrease.
   b) Increasing the pressure will increase the yield of ammonia (four moles of gas on the left-hand side and two moles on the right).
   c) Removing the ammonia will cause the equilibrium to shift to the right thus increasing the yield of ammonia.
5 a) PCl_3 decreases
   b) PCl_3 increases
   c) PCl_3 decreases
   d) PCl_3 decreases

14 Chemical energy

1 $-900\,kJ\,mol^{-1}$
2 $-214\,kJ\,mol^{-1}$
3 $-487\,kJ\,mol^{-1}$
4 $226\,kJ\,mol^{-1}$
5 $-124\,kJ\,mol^{-1}$
6 $-2168\,kJ\,mol^{-1}$
7 a) $-115\,kJ\,mol^{-1}$
   b) $Cl_2(g) \rightarrow Cl^\bullet + Cl^\bullet$

15 Oxidising and reducing agents

1 a) $Mg \rightarrow Mg^{2+} + 2e^-$ (Oxidation); $Ag^+ + e^- \rightarrow Ag$ (Reduction)
   b) $Mg + 2Ag^+ \rightarrow Mg^{2+} + 2Ag$
   c) Mg is the reducing agent; Ag^+ is the oxidising agent.
2 Fluorine, chlorine, calcium and sodium
3 a) $SO_3^{2-} + H_2O \rightarrow SO_4^{2-} + 2H^+ + 2e^-$
   b) $NO_3^- + 4H^+ + 3e^- \rightarrow NO + 2H_2O$
   c) $H_2O_2 \rightarrow O_2 + 2H^+ + 2e^-$
   d) $VO_3^- + 6H^+ + 3e^- \rightarrow V^{2+} + 3H_2O$

4 B (Hint: PbO contains Pb^{2+}. It must have gained $2e^-$ to form Pb.)

5 a) $Fe_2O_3 + 3CO \rightarrow 2Fe + 3CO_2$

   b) $Fe^{3+} + 3e^- \rightarrow Fe$

   c) Reducing agent

16 Chemical analysis

1 a) Pipette

   b) Burette

   c) $0.041 \, mol \, l^{-1}$

2 a) $12.05 \, cm^3$

   b) Using a pipette

   c) 1.205×10^{-4} moles of iodine

   d) $0.21 \, g$

3 a) Tyrosine

   b)

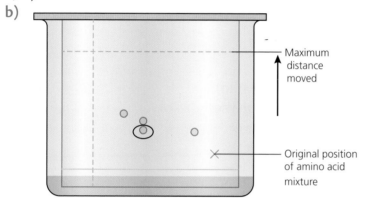

   c) With solvent 1, alanine and threonine have the same R_f value and travel the same distance as a single spot. When they are placed in solvent 2, the spot splits into two since alanine and threonine have different R_f values.

Appendix 1

1 B

2 D

3 The following is a list of possible answers:

   - Carry out an experiment to check the conductivity of molten chocolate. If ionic compounds are present, the molten chocolate should conduct electricity. Go on to discuss why ionic compounds conduct and covalent compounds do not.
   - Discuss the compounds likely to be found in chocolate, for example flavourings such as esters. Show typical ester structures and explain that they are covalent with low mp.
   - Sugars are carbohydrates which are covalent.
   - Aldehydes and ketones could be present; discuss this idea and draw structures.
   - Antioxidants could be present to prevent spoiling. Discuss this idea and draw the structure of a typical antioxidant.

- Check the solubility of the chocolate in water and in other solvents. Describe an experiment to determine the solubility. Polar covalent and ionic compounds would dissolve in water; non-polar compounds would dissolve in non-polar solvents such as hexane. Explain why.
- Discuss electrolysis and how ionic compounds would behave.

4 a) i.   A solution of accurately known concentration

    ii. The weighed sample is dissolved in a small volume of deionised water in a beaker and the solution transferred to a standard flask. The beaker is rinsed and the rinsings are also poured into the standard flask. The flask is made up to the mark, adding the last few drops of water using a dropping pipette. The flask is stoppered and inverted several times to ensure thorough mixing of the solution.

    iii. Tap water contains dissolved salts that may react with sodium fluoride and affect the concentration of the solution.

  b) $2\,mg\,l^{-1}$

  c) Concentration $= 0.0324\,mol\,l^{-1}$

5 The diagram should show the gas bubbling through $NaOH\,(aq)$ to remove $CO_2\,(g)$. The nitrogen gas which bubbles through the $NaOH\,(aq)$ unreacted should be measured by a gas syringe or upturned, graduated test tube/measuring cylinder in water.

Appendix 3

Key words

Activated complex   An unstable arrangement of atoms formed at the maximum of the potential energy barrier during a reaction.

Activation energy   The energy required by colliding molecules to form an activated complex.

Addition   A reaction in which two or more molecules combine to produce a larger molecule and nothing else.

Alcohols   Carbon compounds which contain the hydroxyl functional group, $-OH$.

Aldehydes   Carbon compounds which contain the $-CHO$ functional group. They are formed by oxidation of primary alcohols and they oxidise to produce carboxylic acids.

Alkanes   A **homologous series** of saturated hydrocarbons, general formula C_nH_{2n+2}. The first member is methane, CH_4.

Alkenes   A homologous series of unsaturated hydrocarbons, general formula C_nH_{2n}. Each member contains a carbon–carbon double bond. The first member is ethene, $CH_2=CH_2$.

Alkyl group   A group of carbon and hydrogen atoms forming a branch in a carbon compound, for example methyl group, CH_3-, ethyl group, C_2H_5-.

Amide link   Group of atoms formed by **condensation polymerisation** of amino acids in the formation of protein chains. The amide link is CONH and occurs between each pair of amino acid residues in the chain. Also called a peptide link.

Amine   A compound containing $-NH_2$.

Amino acids   Compounds of general formula, $H_2NCHRCOOH$ – where R is, for example, H, CH_3, $C_6H_5CH_2$ – which link by condensation reaction to form proteins. Essential amino acids cannot be synthesised by an organism and must be present in its diet.

Antioxidants   Compounds that slow oxidation reactions. They are commonly added to food to prevent edible oils becoming rancid. Examples include vitamins E and C.

Atom economy   A measure of the proportion of reactants that have been converted into products. It is calculated by using the formula, atom economy = mass of desired product/total mass of reactants $\times$ 100. Reactions with a high atom economy are desirable.

Atomic number The number of **protons** in the nucleus of an atom.

Average rate The change in mass or concentration of a reactant or product divided by the time interval during which the change occurs.

Biodegrade The breakdown of materials by bacteria or other biological means.

Bonding continuum A concept applied to bonding. Ionic and covalent bonding lie at opposite ends of the bonding continuum with polar covalent bonding in between.

Carbonyl group The carbonyl group is C=O. It is present in ketones and aldehydes.

Carboxyl group The functional group present in carboxylic acids, −COOH.

Carboxylic acids Carbon compounds which contain the carboxyl functional group. Ethanoic acid is an example of a carboxylic acid.

Catalyst A substance which speeds up a reaction without itself being used up. It lowers the activation energy of the reaction.

Chromatography A technique for separating substances. Molecules of different size or polarity can be separated by this technique which uses a **mobile phase** of gas or liquid passing over a **stationary phase** of a solid or a liquid-impregnated solid.

Closed system Reversible reactions will only reach a state of dynamic equilibrium when the reaction takes place in a reaction vessel which prevents reactants and products escaping.

Collision geometry A term used to describe the way reactants collide with each other.

Collision theory A theory used to explain the factors which lead to a successful reaction. It explains how altering **variables**, such as temperature, can affect the speed of the reaction. The theory requires reactants to i) collide, ii) have the correct collision geometry and iii) have a minimum energy (the activation energy) before a reaction occurs.

Concentration The amount of solute dissolved in a given volume of solution. The usual units are moles per litre ($mol\, l^{-1}$).

Condensation polymerisation A process whereby many small molecules (monomers) join to form a large molecule (a **polymer**), with water or other small molecules formed at the same time. Forming a protein from amino acids is an example of condensation polymerisation.

Condensation reaction A reaction in which two (or more) molecules join together by the elimination of a small molecule, such as water.

Covalent bonding Bond formed between two atoms by the sharing of a pair of electrons. This usually occurs between non-metal atoms.

Covalent molecular   A description of the structure and bonding in small molecules, for example Cl_2 and H_2O.

Covalent network   A very strong and stable structure formed by certain elements (such as B, C diamond and Si) and certain compounds (for example, SiC and SiO_2). All the atoms are held together by strong covalent bonds. Consequently, covalent network compounds are all solids at room temperature and have very high melting points.

Covalent radius   A useful measure of atomic size, being half the distance between the nuclei of two covalently bonded atoms of an element. Covalent bond lengths between any two atoms can be obtained by adding the appropriate covalent atomic radii.

Cycloalkanes   A homologous series of saturated ring molecules with general formula C_nH_{2n}. The simplest is cyclopropane, C_3H_6.

Dehydration   The removal of water from a single compound, for example dehydration of ethanol, C_2H_5OH, produces ethene, C_2H_4.

Delocalised electrons   Electrons which are not confined to a single orbital between a pair of atoms, for example in metallic bonding. Delocalised electrons are free to move away from the atom they came from.

Denaturing/Denature   Altering the shape of a protein by an increase in temperature or a reduction in pH. Loss of enzyme activity is one important consequence.

Detergent   A soap-like molecule which can dissolve fats and oils. Unlike soaps, detergents do not contain a carboxylate (COO^-) head.

Displacement   A redox reaction where a metal high in the electrochemical series reacts with a metal compound lower in the electrochemical series.

Distillation   A process used for separating liquid mixtures. A liquid is boiled and its vapour then condensed to collect pure samples of the liquid. It is used to increase the percentage of ethanol after **fermentation.**

Electrochemical series   A list of chemicals arranged in order of their increasing ability to gain electrons, in other words in order of increasing oxidising power.

Electrolysis   The process which occurs when a current of electricity is passed through a molten electrolyte (resulting in decomposition) or an electrolyte solution (which results in decomposition of the solute and/or the water).

Electron   A particle which moves around the nucleus of an atom. It has a single negative charge but its mass is negligible compared to that of a proton or neutron.

Electronegativity The strength of the attraction by an atom of an element for its bonding electrons. If the electronegativities of two atoms sharing electrons are similar, the bond will be almost purely covalent. The greater the difference in electronegativities, the more likely the bond is to be polar covalent or even ionic.

Emulsifier A compound which allows oil and water to mix.

Emulsion A mixture of liquids where small droplets of one liquid are dispersed in another liquid. Emulsions of oil and water are commonly found in food.

Endothermic reaction A reaction in which heat energy is absorbed from the surroundings. It has a positive enthalpy change (ΔH).

End-point The point in a titration where the indicator changes colour to indicate that the reaction is complete.

Enthalpy change The difference in heat energy between reactants and products in a reaction.

Enthalpy of combustion The enthalpy change when one mole of a substance is completely burned in oxygen.

Enzyme A globular protein which is able to catalyse a specific reaction.

Equilibrium State attained in a reversible reaction when forward and reverse reactions are taking place at the same rate.

Essential amino acids Amino acids which cannot be made by the body. They must be obtained from the diet.

Essential oils Oils extracted from plants. They usually have distinctive smells, are non-polar, volatile and contain compounds known as terpenes.

Esters Carbon compounds formed when alcohols react with carboxylic acids by condensation.

Exothermic reaction A reaction in which heat energy is released to the surroundings. It has a negative enthalpy change (ΔH).

Fats Esters formed from one molecule of glycerol and three molecules of, usually saturated, long-chain carboxylic acids. The compounds have melting points high enough to be solid at room temperature. See also **oils.**

Fatty acids Carboxylic acids formed from the hydrolysis of fats and oils.

Feedstock A substance derived from a **raw material** which is used to manufacture another substance.

Fermentation The process catalysed by enzymes in yeast which converts sugars into ethanol and carbon dioxide. This is known as alcoholic fermentation.

Free radicals Highly reactive atoms or molecules with unpaired electrons.

Free radical scavenger   A compound added to plastics, cosmetics and foods to prevent free radical reactions. These scavengers react with free radicals to produce stable molecules. This terminates the reaction.

Functional group   A group of atoms or type of carbon–carbon bond which provides a series of carbon compounds with its characteristic chemical properties, for example –CHO, –C=C–.

Gas liquid chromatography (GLC)   A technique used to separate mixtures in the gas phase.

Glycerol   Propane-1,2,3-triol; formed from the hydrolysis of fats and oils.

Group   A column of elements in the Periodic Table. The values of a selected physical property show a distinct trend of increase or decrease down the column. The chemical properties of the elements in the group are similar.

Haber process   The industrial production of ammonia from nitrogen and hydrogen using high pressure and temperature, with iron as a catalyst.

Hess's law   The enthalpy change of a chemical reaction depends only on the chemical nature and physical state of the reactants and products and is independent of any intermediate steps.

Homologous series   A group of chemically similar compounds which can be represented by a general formula. Physical properties change progressively through the series, for example the alkanes, general formula C_nH_{2n+2}, show a steady increase in boiling point.

Hormones   Chemicals, often complex proteins, which regulate metabolic processes in the body. An example is insulin which regulates sugar metabolism.

Hydration   The addition of water to an unsaturated compound, for example the hydration of ethene, C_2H_4, produces ethanol, C_2H_5OH.

Hydrocarbon   A compound containing the elements carbon and hydrogen only.

Hydrogenation   The addition of hydrogen to an unsaturated compound; for example hydrogenation converts alkenes to alkanes and oils into fats.

Hydrogen bonds/bonding   Intermolecular forces of attraction. The molecules must contain highly polar bonds in which hydrogen atoms are linked to very electronegative nitrogen, oxygen or fluorine atoms. The hydrogen atoms are then left with a positive charge and are attracted to the electronegative atoms of other molecules. They are a specific, stronger type of permanent dipole–permanent dipole interaction.

Hydrolysis   The breaking down of larger molecules into smaller molecules by reaction with water.

Hydrophilic A term used to describe molecules, or parts of a molecule, which are attracted to water. For example, the –OH group in alcohols is hydrophilic.

Hydrophobic A term used to describe molecules, or parts of a molecule, which repel water and will not bond to water. For example, the long hydrocarbon chains in fats and oils are hydrophobic.

Hydroxyl group The –OH group; it is found in alcohols.

Indicator A chemical dye added to a titration to detect the end-point.

Intermolecular bonds/bonding Bonds between molecules, such as London dispersion forces, permanent dipole–permanent dipole interactions and hydrogen bonds. They are much weaker than **intramolecular** bonds.

Intramolecular bonds Bonds within molecules, such as covalent and polar covalent bonds.

Ion–electron equation Equation which shows either the loss of electrons (oxidation) or the gain of electrons (reduction).

Ionic bond Bond formed as a result of attraction between positive and negative ions.

Ionisation The loss or gain of electrons by neutral atoms to form ions, for example

$$Na(g) \rightarrow Na^+(g) + e^-$$
$$Cl(g) + e^- \rightarrow Cl^-(g)$$

'Ionisation enthalpy' is usually reserved for enthalpy changes referring to the formation of positive ions.

Ionisation energy The energy required to remove 1 mole of electrons from 1 mole of atoms in the gaseous state.

Ions Atoms or groups of atoms which possess a positive or negative charge due to loss or gain of electrons, for example Na^+ and CO_3^{2-}.

Isomers Compounds which have the same molecular formula but different structural formulae.

Isotopes Atoms of the same element which have different numbers of **neutrons**. They have the same atomic number but different **mass numbers**.

Ketones Carbon compounds which contain the carbonyl group (C=O). They are formed from the oxidation of secondary alcohols. Unlike aldehydes, ketones cannot be oxidised using mild oxidising agents.

Lattice The three-dimensional arrangement of positive and negative ions in the solid, crystalline state of ionic compounds.

Le Chatelier's principle   If any change of physical or chemical conditions is imposed on any chemical equilibrium then the equilibrium alters in the direction which tends to counteract the change of conditions.

London dispersion force   A force of attraction between all atoms and molecules formed from temporary and induced dipoles.

Mass number   The total number of protons and neutrons in the nucleus of an atom.

Metallic bonding   The bonding responsible for typical metallic properties such as malleability, ductility and electrical conductivity in metals and alloys. Each atom loses its outer electrons to form positive ions. These ions pack together in a regular crystalline arrangement with the electrons delocalised through the structure, binding the ions together.

Miscibility   The ability of liquids to mix perfectly together. In contrast, immiscible liquids form clearly defined layers with the denser liquid forming the lower layer.

Mobile phase   In chromatography, the moving part of the process; for example the inert gas in GLC which carries the mixture of compounds through the column, or the solvent in paper chromatography which carries the mixture of compounds up the paper.

Molar bond enthalpy   The energy required to break one mole of covalent bonds. Values are listed in the data booklet.

Molar volume   The volume of one mole of a gas at a specified temperature and pressure.

Mole   The gram formula mass of a substance. It contains 6.02×10^{23} formula units of the substance. The commonly used abbreviation for mole is 'mol'.

Molecular formula   Formula which shows the number of atoms of the different elements which are present in one molecule of a substance.

Molecule   A group of atoms held together by covalent bonds.

Monatomic   A term used to describe the noble gases since they are composed of individual atoms which do not bond to each other. They are held together by London dispersion forces in the liquid and solid state.

Neutron   A particle found in the nucleus of an atom. It has the same mass as a proton but no charge.

Non-polar covalent bond   A covalent bond where both atoms share the electrons equally. This occurs between all elements that exist as molecules, such as Cl_2 and S_8, since the atoms joining are identical. It also occurs in compounds where the bonding atoms have a small difference in electronegativity, such as hydrocarbons.

Nucleus   The extremely small centre of an atom where the neutrons and protons are found.

Oils   Esters formed from one molecule of glycerol and three molecules of, usually unsaturated, carboxylic acids. Oils have melting points low enough to be liquid at normal room temperature. See **fats.**

Oxidation   A process in which electrons are lost.

Oxidising agent   A substance which gains electrons, in other words is an electron acceptor.

Peptide link   See **amide link.**

Percentage yield   This is the actual yield of substance obtained divided by the theoretical yield calculated from the balanced equation then multiplied by 100.

Period   A horizontal row in the Periodic Table.

Periodic Table   An arrangement of the elements in order of increasing atomic number, with chemically similar elements occurring in the same main vertical columns (groups).

Permanent dipole–permanent dipole interactions   The attraction between molecules which possess a permanent dipole because of the presence of polar bonds.

pH   A measure of the acidity of a solution.

Polar covalent bonds   Bonds formed between non-metallic atoms by sharing a pair of electrons. If the atoms have considerably different electronegativities, the electrons are not shared equally, the more electronegative atom becoming slightly negative in comparison to the other atom. As a result the bond is 'polar', for example $H^{\delta+}–Cl^{\delta-}$.

Polymer A very large molecule which is formed by the joining together of many smaller molecules (monomers).

Polymerisation The process whereby a polymer is formed.

Proton A particle found in the nucleus of an atom. It has a single positive charge and the same mass as a neutron.

Rate of reaction A measure of the speed of a chemical reaction.

Raw material A useful substance for the chemical industry which found naturally, for example crude oil, water, air, metallic ores, coal, etc. Feedstocks are obtained from raw materials.

Redox reaction   A reaction in which reduction and oxidation take place. Electrons are lost by one substance and gained by another.

Redox titration   An experiment in which the volumes of aqueous solutions of a reducing agent and an oxidising agent, which react together completely, are measured accurately. The concentration of one of the reactants can then be determined provided the concentration of the other reactant is known.

Reducing agent   A substance which loses electrons, in other words an electron donor.

Reduction   A process in which electrons are gained.

Relative atomic mass   The average mass of one atom of an element on a scale where one atom of $^{12}_{6}C$ has a mass of 12 units exactly.

Relative rate   Reciprocal of time, i.e. $\dfrac{1}{time}$

Reproducibility   Results obtained from an experiment are said to be reproducible if the same data can be obtained when the experiment is repeated. An experiment with good reproducibility will produce the same results when carried out again and again.

Retention time   The length of time it takes a substance to reach the detector, in a chromatography experiment, after being injected into the chromatography column.

Reversible reaction   One which proceeds in both directions, for example:

$$N_2 + 3H_2 \rightleftharpoons 2NH_3$$

Rogue data   Results obtained from an experiment that are unusual/do not fit the pattern of expected results. Usually caused by experimental error.

Saturated compound   A compound in which all carbon–carbon covalent bonds are single bonds.

Screening   The ability of electrons in the inner energy levels of an atom to reduce the attraction of the nuclear charge for the electrons of the outermost levels.

Spectator ion   An ion which is present in a reaction mixture but takes no part in the reaction.

Standard solution   A solution of known concentration.

State symbols   Symbols used to indicate the state of atoms, ions or molecules: (s) = solid; (l) = liquid; (g) = gas; (aq) = aqueous (dissolved in water).

Stationary phase   In chromatography, the phase other than the mobile phase. For example, the liquid in GLC.

Structural formula   A formula which shows the arrangement of atoms in a molecule or ion. A full structural formula shows all of the bonds. A shortened structural formula shows the sequence of groups of atoms.

Temporary dipole   Formed in all atoms where an excess of electrons is formed at one part of the atom. Temporary dipoles are the basis for London dispersion forces.

Terpene   Unsaturated compounds found in many plant oils. They are formed from the joining together of isoprene units.

Transition metals   The elements which form a 'bridge' in the Periodic Table between groups II and III; for example, iron and copper.

Triglyceride   The molecules found in fats and oils. They are formed from one glycerol molecule joining to three fatty acid molecules.

Ultraviolet light   A high-energy form of radiation which can break bonds in molecules, causing free radicals to form.

Unsaturated compounds   Compounds in which there are carbon–carbon double or triple bonds, such as alkenes, alkynes and vegetable oils.

Van der Waals' forces   The forces of attraction that occur between all atoms and molecules. They are known as intermolecular forces and include hydrogen bonding, permanent dipole–permanent dipole interactions and London dispersion forces. Van der Waals' forces are much weaker than covalent bonds.

Variable   Something that can be changed in a chemical reaction, such as temperature, particle size, concentration, etc.

Viscosity/viscous   A description of how 'thick' a liquid is, for example engine oil is 'thicker' (more viscous) than petrol.